MUSIC WORKOUT

Grade 7

Jean Archibald and Bernadette Marmion

Royal Irish Academy of Music

INTRODUCTION

Music Workout Grade 7 differs in organisation from previous books in the series where topics were studied consecutively. In this book it is recommended that the three parts should be studied concurrently so that a varied course is provided. As in the other books the signal ● shows where new concepts and information are introduced; ■ indicates suggestions, points to be memorised and useful hints.

CONTENTS

Part 1

Sight Singing Melody Writing Song Writing

Part 2

Harmony : Cadences and 2-part Writing

Part 3

Rudiments History Score Reading Aural/Visual Observation

PART 1

SINGING with SOLFA

■ These tunes provide revision in major and minor keys. The length is expanded to 8 bars with occasional semiquaver rhythm added.

Exercise 1 Sing these tunes using solfa names. Tap a steady beat as you sing.

MELODY WRITING

■ Revise 8-bar melody writing by studying this summary.

1 Opening Sing the given opening a few times to assess its style and character. These are the seeds from which the melody will grow.

2 Rhythm / Phrasing A good rhythmic framework is vital. It is the peg on which the entire melody hangs. A 4-bar phrase is the most natural length, so simple 8-bar melodies usually divide evenly with 2 main phrases of 4 + 4. Longer 4-bar phrases may subdivide into 2 + 2. A long note value in bars 4 and 8 helps to give the sense of phrase ending. When the given phrase begins with an up-beat, it is probable that all subsequent phrases will do also. This gives a natural rhythmic balance between the phrases. Remember to draw in the phrase marks.

3 Pitch Write a melodic shape which you can sing confidently. The finished piece should have a natural, interesting and balanced shape, and a strong sense of direction, as though making a journey out and returning home to the tonic at the end.

4 Tempo / Expression Remember to add these to the finished piece. An 8-bar melody generally does not need many expression marks. It is helpful to ask yourself: " Will the expression marks included enhance the music in performance?"

Exercise 2 Using the given opening, compose a melody to make a total of 8 bars. Phrase the finished melody and include marks of tempo and expression.

LEAPS between NOTES of the DOMINANT CHORD

- In the early stages of sight-singing the focus was on leaps between the notes of the tonic chord. Now leaps between notes of the dominant chord are included, some of which you have met already. In these drills the bracketed notes belong to the dominant chord and show the different combinations of leaps within it.
  - The sound is the same in major and minor keys. Both are given to show the solfa names.

Exercise 3 Practise singing these drills with solfa to learn the new intervals.

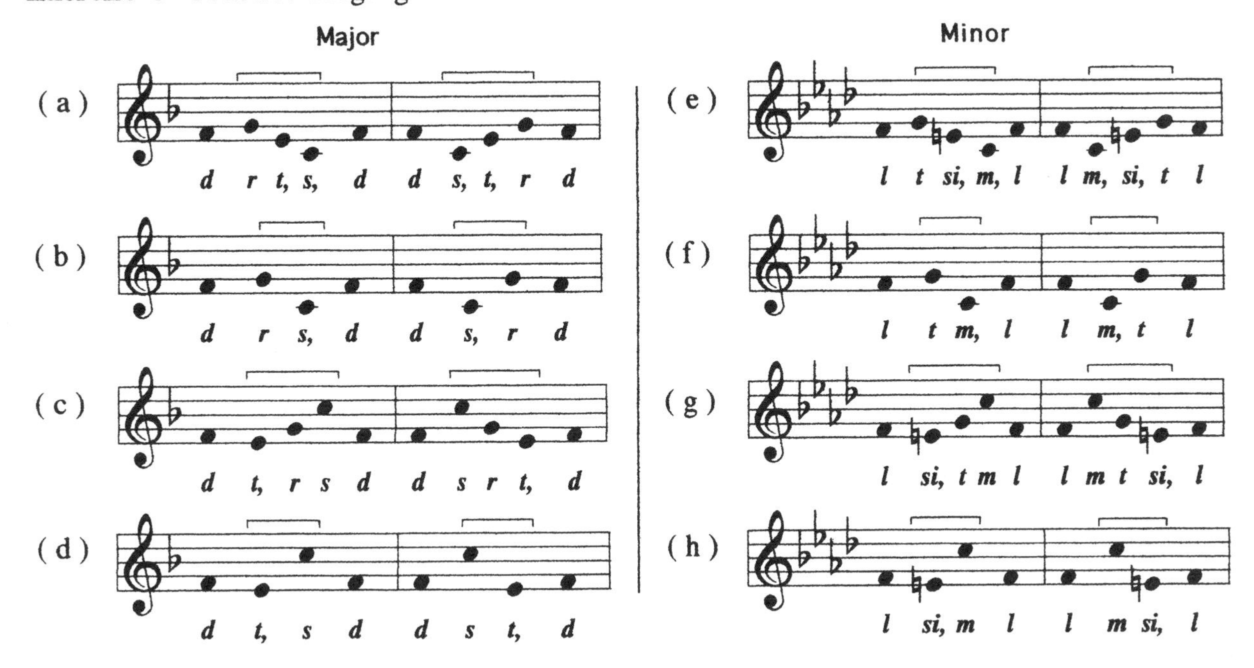

Exercise 4 Watch for leaps between notes of the dominant chord in these. Tap a steady beat.

MELODIES with MODULATION to RELATIVE MAJOR / MINOR

- To **modulate** is to **change key** during the course of a piece of music. This detour to another key brings a change of colour to the music by the accidentals it introduces. Modulation is possible to a wide range of keys but the simplest modulation is between related keys, i.e. from a major key to its relative minor and from a minor key to its relative major. These modulations will be studied first.

This tune is in C major. Sing it using solfa names. It changes briefly to A minor by introducing *si* in bar 4. *So* is heard again in bar 5 as the tune returns to C major.

This tune is in A minor. It modulates to its relative major. Sing it with solfa names.

Bars 1 - 4 are in A minor. Bar 5/6 modulates to C major by introducing *so*. The tune returns to A minor when *si* is heard again in bar 7.

Exercise 5 Sing these with solfa names. Note key changes. They are marked in (a) and (b).

ADDING A MODULATING PHRASE : Major to Relative Minor

Modulation is a useful tool when writing longer melodies. Later in this section melody writing will be expanded to 12 bars. A 12-bar melody (4 + 4 + 4) is often constructed like a sandwich with the interest in the middle, i.e. the outer phrases are in the tonic while a modulation is introduced in the middle phrase.

These exercises are a first stage in writing 12-bar melodies. The melodies, of which the first complete phrase is given, are in major keys. You are to write another phrase which modulates to the relative minor. To do this, introduce *si* and end the phrase on *la.* If you want to use the melodic minor, include *fi* with *si.*

Exercise 6 Sing the given phrase. Continue by composing another 4-bar phrase which modulates to the relative minor. Finish on *la*, the new tonic, in bar 8.

ADDING A MODULATING PHRASE : Minor to Relative Major

- In order to modulate from a minor key to its relative major, *so* is introduced. The major key is established by ending the phrase on *do*.

Exercise 7 Sing the given phrases, all of which are in minor keys. Continue each by composing another 4-bar phrase which modulates to the relative major. Finish on *do*, the new tonic, in bar 8.

COMPLETING all the LEAPS of a 3rd

- You have already learnt to sing many intervals of a 3rd in different areas of the scale. Those not already covered in the context of a major key are marked * in this drill. Sing it several times until all the intervals are familiar.

This variation of the drill shows all the 3rds in a harmonic minor scale. Intervals marked * are now included in the minor key. Sing the pattern using solfa names.

Exercise 8 Sing these melodies. The last two exercises modulate briefly to the relative key.

MELODIES with MODULATION to the DOMINANT : MAJOR KEYS

- The most common modulation from a major key is to its dominant, e.g. C major modulating to G major. A modulation to the dominant key makes the sound 'brighter' because of the raised accidental it introduces.

  Sing this well-known carol melody which modulates to the dominant at the halfway point. The new raised accidental is *fi*.

fi - *s* is the signal for a modulation to the dominant key. The melody returns to the tonic when *f* is heard again.

Exercise 9 Sing these melodies using solfa. Note where each modulates to the dominant key.

ADDING a MODULATING PHRASE : MAJOR to DOMINANT

● The easiest way to deal with the new accidental *fi* is to approach it by step and follow it by *s*. When you become more confident in modulating, this procedure can be relaxed.

The given phrase of each of these exercises is the opening phrase of a folk song. The folk song continues with a modulation to the dominant in its second phrase. In Exercise 10 you compose your own second phrase modulating to the dominant.

Exercise 10 Having sung the given phrase, continue the melody by composing another 4-bar phrase which modulates to the dominant key. Finish the phrase on *s* in in bar 8. Add phrasing.

COMPLETING ALL LEAPS of a PERFECT 4th

- Practise singing this drill to learn all the perfect 4ths in a major key. The new intervals are marked * .

In the minor key, two intervals of a perfect 4th remain which have not been included already. Use this short pattern to practise singing them.

Exercise 11 As you sing these melodies look out for the new intervals of a 4th. Most of the melodies also include a brief modulation to the relative or dominant key.

MELODIES with MODULATION to the DOMINANT : Minor Keys

A modulation to the dominant always creates a 'brighter' sound . This is because the dominant key is on the sharp side of the tonic. This is true for minor keys as well as major, e.g. C major —> G major ; A minor —> E minor.

A major key modulates to its dominant by introducing one new accidental *fi*. When a <u>minor</u> key modulates to its dominant, it modulates to another <u>minor</u> key. As a result further accidentals in addition to *fi* are needed.

Note these points about the accidentals.

fi is always present in a modulation to the dominant key.

ri is introduced as the raised 7th of the new minor key.

si becomes *s* as the old raised 7th is cancelled.

The new accidentals *fi* and *ri* are drawn towards *m* as the dominant modulation is established.

Sing this melody which begins in A minor and modulates to E minor.

Exercise 12 Sing these minor key melodies which include modulation to the dominant. The change of key and solfa names for the accidentals are given in the first examples.

ADDING A MODULATING PHRASE : Minor to Dominant

- When modulating from a minor key to the dominant, the easiest way to manage the new accidentals *fi* and *ri* is to introduce them in a stepwise shape e.g. *s* - *fi* - *m*; *m* - *ri* - *m*. Establish the new key by finishing on *m*.

Exercise 13 In each case, having sung the given minor key phrase, continue the melody by composing another 4-bar phrase which modulates to the dominant key. Finish the phrase on *m* in bar 8. Add phrasing.

COMPLETING ALL LEAPS of a PERFECT 5th

- Practise singing this drill to learn all the perfect 5ths in a major key. The new intervals are marked * .

The two remaining intervals of a perfect 5th not already included in a minor key are marked * in the following short pattern. Sing the pattern a few times.

Exercis 14 Sing the following melodies using solfa. Look out for the intervals of a 5th as well as modulation to the relative and dominant keys.

WRITING a 12-bar MELODY with MODULATION

- You have learned to write the first two phrases of a longer melody with the initial phrase in the tonic key and a modulation in the second. Add a further 4-bar phrase which returns to and finishes in the tonic key and you have a simple12-bar structure. We continue our study with this length of melody, though 12-bar melodies are less usual than 8-bar or 16-bar ones.

  A well balanced melody will use some repeated features to hold its phrases together in a unified way. Sing the following examples and note the points made about their individual design.

This example has a simple 'sandwich' structure. The outer phrases show a strong similarity while the middle phrase provides some contrast.

Example 2 also shows a 'sandwich' structure but here the similarity between the first and third phrases is less striking.

This has a looser structure in which the second phrase answers the first. Also,the shape of the last phrase is unlike that of the first two phrases.

The three contrasting phrases here are held together by short repeated ideas.

12- Bar MELODY : EXERCISES

■ These exercises should be done on manuscript paper.

Exercise 15 Transcribe each opening. Then continue each to make a 12-bar melody. Include a modulation as indicated. Add phrasing, tempo and expression marks to each completed melody.

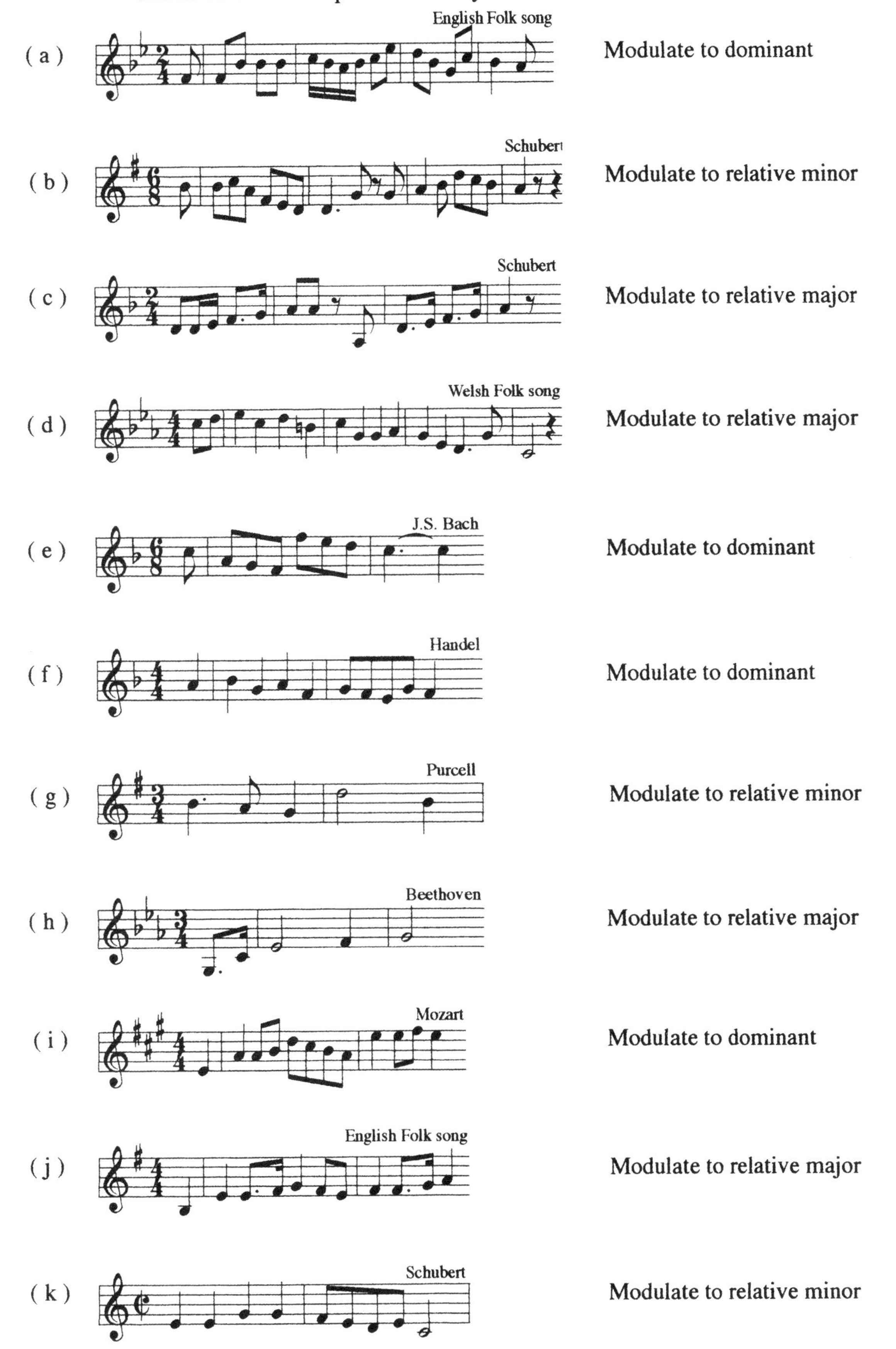

SONG WRITING

■ Revise word rhythms and melody writing in *Music Workout Grade 5* and *Grade 6.*

● **New tunes for old** Writing a tune to words combines word rhythm and melody writing. A song is just word rhythm 'clothed' in melody. This type of composition is called **word setting** - the words are 'set' to music.

In a simple song like *Baa, baa, black sheep* the rhythm is:

Clothing this rhythm in melody gives

Here is the same word rhythm, but set to a new melody in a new key.

Exercise 16 Write five new tunes for *Baa, baa, black sheep.* The opening notes are given. In each case be sure to end on the tonic.

(a)

(b)

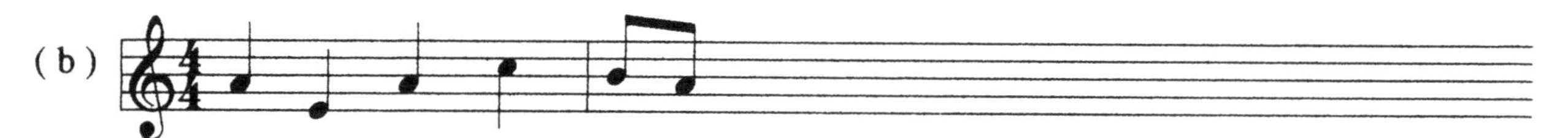

(c)

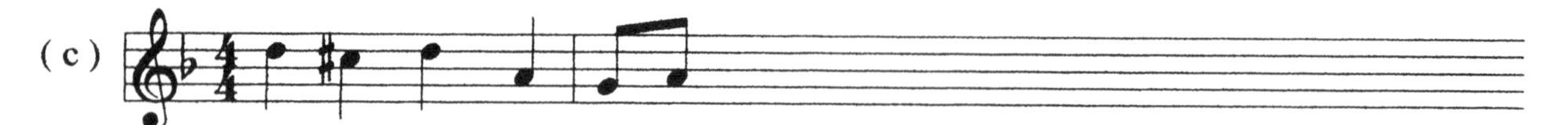

(d)

(e)

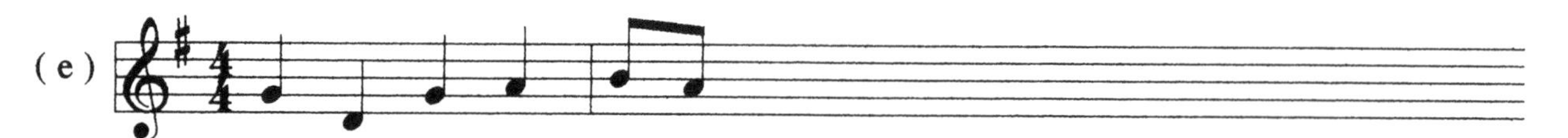

● **Four-bar Melodies** The next stage is to set the following to music.

Piping down the valleys wild, Piping songs of pleasant glee. William Blake

Saying this aloud, the accents seem to fall as follows:

Píping down the válleys wild, Píping songs of pléasant glee.

This produces 4 accents, i.e. 4 bar lines, a normal phrase length. With bar lines before these accented syllables, a simple rhythm could be

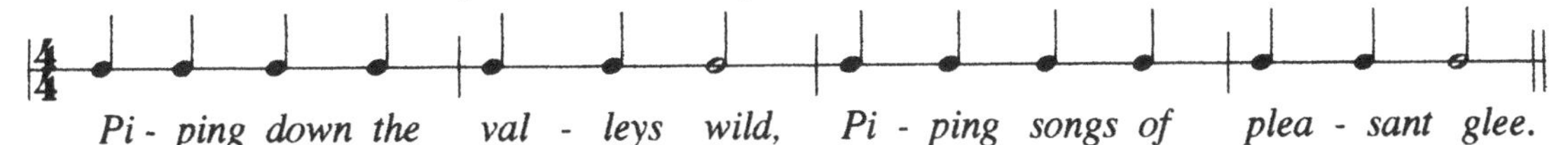

Rhythmic variety can be obtained by using quavers for unimportant words such as 'the' and 'of '.

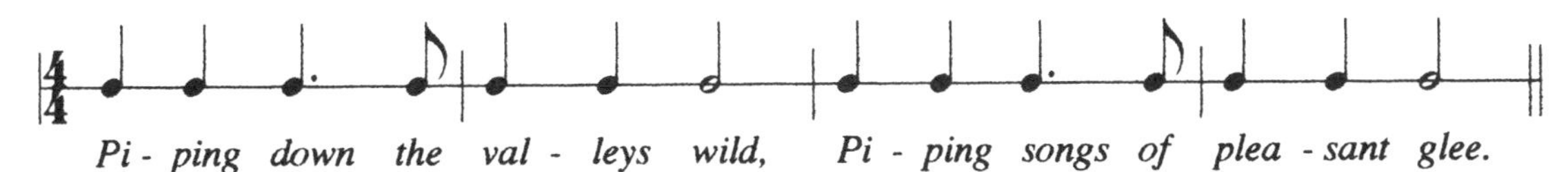

Clothing the rhythm in melody

Exercise 17 Set the following phrases to music, ending on the tonic in each case. The openings are given. First, work out the rhythm on the upper stave. Then write your melody, making two 2-bar phrases.

● **Melodies with Upbeats** Probably more stanzas of poetry commence with upbeats than with strong accents. In any melody, if the first phrase begins with an upbeat, the second is likely to also.

Study this folksong extract. Each 2-bar phrase begins with an upbeat.

4-bar phrases may also begin with upbeats as in this example.

Exercise 18 Write 4-bar rhythms, then melodies, to match these words, using the given openings. Accented syllables come first in a bar. End on the tonic.

- **Melismata** The term **melisma** describes a group of notes sung to one syllable. (Greek: *melisma* = song; plural *melismata*). The term is used to distinguish this from singing one note per syllable, which is what has been used till now. The simplest tunes use one note per syllable; using melismata can create a more flowing and interesting melody. The most common melisma is a pair of quavers. Study these versions of the Welsh folk song '*The Ash Grove*'.

(**A**) has one note per syllable, (**B**) has melismatic quavers. Sing both for comparison. The second seems smoother. Note that slurs are placed over notes of a melisma to show they belong to one syllable. In compound time, e.g. $\frac{6}{8}$, two quavers are often allotted to a syllable. Study this example.

In some editions of vocal music, tailed notes are not beamed except when they belong to the same syllable. In such a case, the extract would look like this:

■ For the time being, however, maybe it is better to follow normal grouping rules.

Exercise 19 Decorate these tunes by substituting 2-note melismata as you think suitable. Rewrite the new version on the lower stave, complete with words and slurs.

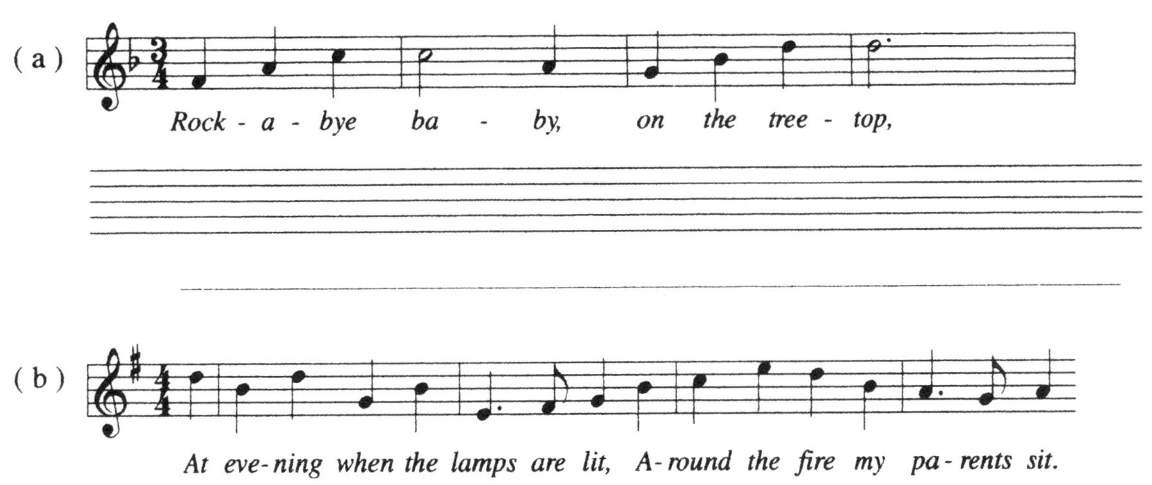

SETTING 4 - LINE STANZAS

The most common poetry stanza has 4 lines. When setting 4-line stanzas, while matching words to rhythm, the form of the melody must be considered. Sing these examples, noting their form. Phrases are labelled **A, B, C, D**, so that any which is repeated can be identified. The label **A**d, **B**d, etc. (d = development) shows where a phrase has been changed a little, but is still recognisable as **A** or **B**, etc.

As printed below, there are 2 lines of poetry on each stave. Remember that a new poetry line begins with a capital letter. Check for the repeated phrase in each case.

Did you notice the following points about the melodies?

1 In $\frac{2}{4}$ and $\frac{3}{4}$ time, 4-bar phrases are likely. In $\frac{4}{4}$ time, 2-bar phrases are also possible.

2 For syllables with melismata, a line like a long hyphen is often added in the text.

Example Follow this plan. Use music manuscript paper as a lot of space is needed.

1 For each line of poetry, use two staves. The upper stave is for the rhythm, the lower for the melody.

2 Write the rhythm first on the upper stave.

3 Decide on the key, keeping within a reasonably singable range.

4 Choose the form. Here it is **A B Ad C** .

5 Check for upbeats.

6 Decide which words might be enhanced by melismata.

7 Suggestions
   (a) Begin on a note of the tonic chord.
   (b) Have a note of the dominant at the half way point.
   (c) End on the tonic.

Exercise 20 Following the example above, set these stanzas to music.

(a) Mary had a little lamb,
Its fleece was white as snow;
And everywhere that Mary went,
The lamb was sure to go. Hale

(b) There are twelve months in all the year,
As I hear many men say.
But the merriest month in all the year
Is the merry month of May. Anon

(c) There was a jolly miller once lived on the River Dee.
He danced and sang from morn to night, no lark so blithe as he;
And this the burden of his song forever used to be,
"I care for nobody, no, not I, if nobody cares for me." Bickerstaffe

(d) Evening red and morning gray
Are the signs of a bonny day.
Evening gray and morning red
Bring down rain on the farmer's head. Anon.

(e) There was an old owl who lived in an oak ;
The more he heard, the less he spoke.
The less he spoke, the more he heard.
Why aren't we like that wise old bird! Anon.

(f) There was a little girl who had a little curl
Right in the middle of her forehead.
And when she was good, she was very,very good,
But when she was bad, she was horrid. 'Jemima' H.W. Longfellow

(g) Her skirt was of the grass-green silk,
Her mantle of the velvet fine;
On every lock of her horse's mane
Hung fifty silver bells and nine. 'True Thomas' Anon

(h) I sprang to the stirrup, and Joris and he;
I galloped, Dirck galloped, we galloped all three;
" Good speed!" cried the watch, as the gate bolts undrew,
"Speed!" echoed the wall to us galloping through. '..The Good News ..' R.Browning

(i) Into the street the piper stept,
Smiling first a little smile.
As if he knew what magic slept
In his quiet pipe the while; ' The Pied Piper of Hamelin' R. Browning

(j) He comes in the night, he comes in the night,
He softly silently comes
While the little brown heads on the pillows so white
Are dreaming of bugles and drums. Anon.

(k) How do you like to go up in a swing!
Up in the air so blue?
Oh, I do think it the pleasantest thing
Ever a child can do ! R.L.Stevenson

(l) Faster than fairies, faster than witches,
Bridges and houses, hedges and ditches;
And charging along like troops in a battle,
All through the meadows the horses and cattle R.L.Stevenson

PART 2

REVISION : 4 - PART CHORDS

■ In Grade 6 you learned to write for S. A. T. B. choir using the primary chords in major and minor keys. This is a summary of the main points.

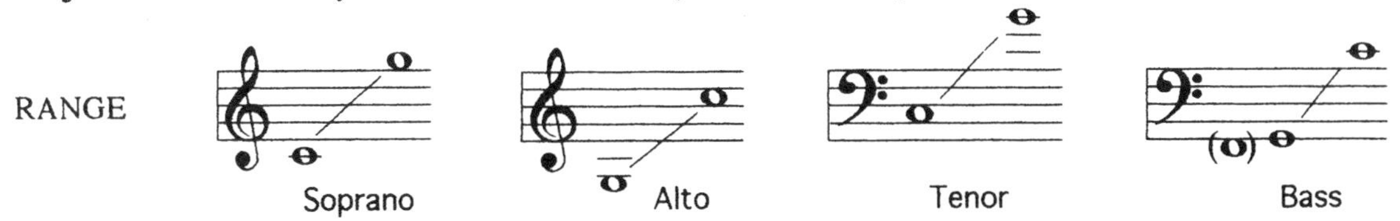

DOUBLING Normally double the root note.

SPACING Any gap wider than an octave should normally only occur between tenor and bass parts. The gap can then be as wide as an octave + 5th.

ROOT POSITION The lowest sounding note should be the root of the chord.

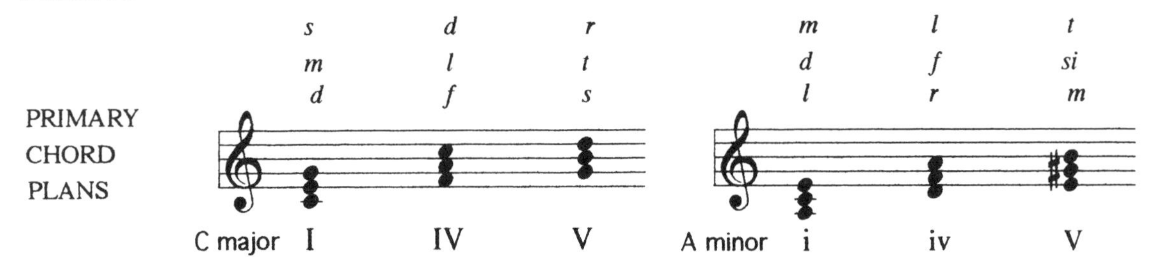

Exercise 21 Complete each chord plan. Write root position chords for S.A.T.B. as shown.

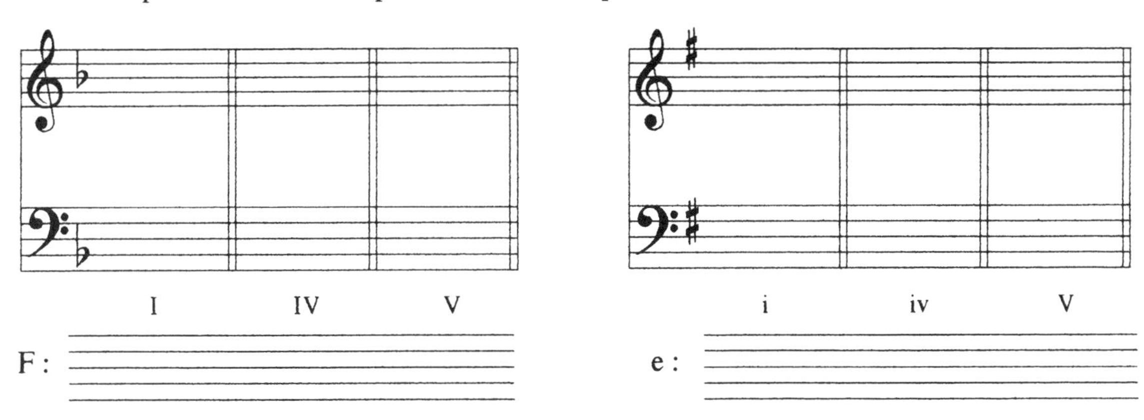

Exercise 22 Sketch a chord plan for each key. Write a numeral below each bass note. Complete each chord by writing notes for S. A. T.

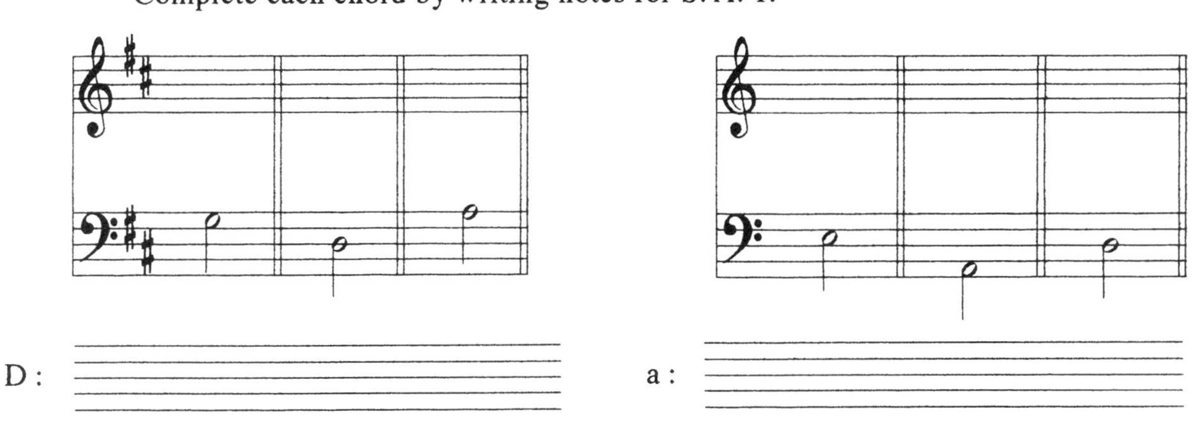

TRIAD TYPES : MAJOR KEYS

■ Differences in the quality of the intervals in triads produce 4 types of triad - major, minor, augmented and diminished. These are summarised below:

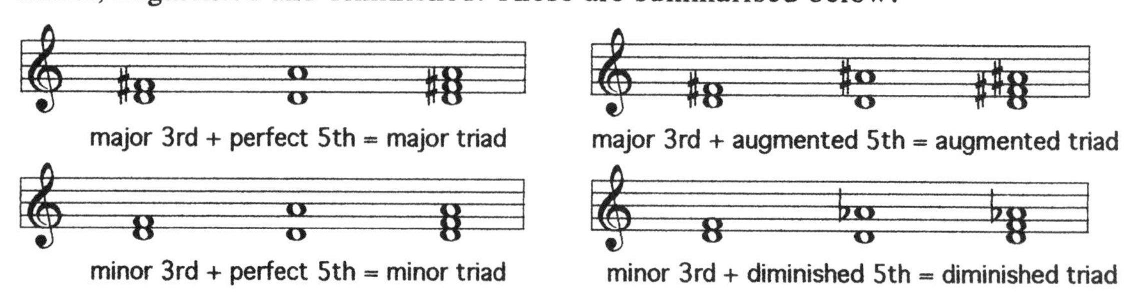

● You know how a triad can be built on any degree of a scale: tonic, dominant, etc. and how to write the primary triads. Now all the triads in a major key are examined to see if their type can be worked out. Study this diagram.

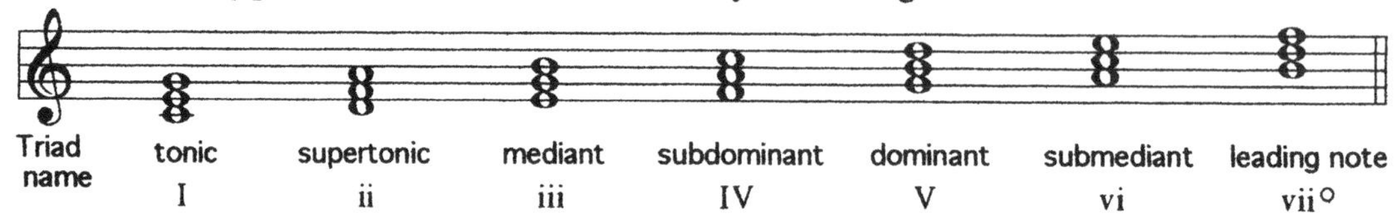

In a major key I , IV and V are all major triads. The supertonic, mediant and submediant triads all consist of a minor 3rd and a perfect 5th and are therefore minor - notice the small numerals. The leading note triad has a minor 3rd but a diminished 5th and is therefore a diminished triad - notice the circle indicating this. Listen to the triads above. Then practise singing this exercise.

■ **Learn** The pattern of triad types in major keys is
Major Minor Minor Major Major Minor Diminished

Exercise 23 All triads in each line belong to the same major key. For each i) Write its name, i.e. name the scale degree on which it is built. ii) State its type - major, minor, augmented or diminished. iii) Give its roman numeral.

(a)

Triad name *Tonic* ________________________________

Triad type *major* ________________________________

Numeral I ________________________________

(b)

Triad name ________________________________

Triad type ________________________________

Numeral ________________________________

TRIAD TYPES : MINOR KEYS

- These are the triads built on minor scale degrees. They are given in C minor for comparison with the C major triads on the opposite page.

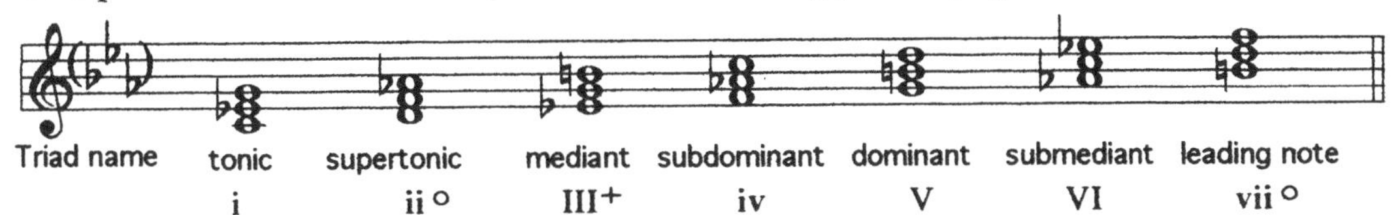

N.B. i and iv have minor 3rds and perfect 5ths and are therefore <u>minor</u>.

V and VI have major 3rds and perfect 5ths and are therefore <u>major</u>.

ii° and vii° have minor 3rds and diminished 5ths and are therefore <u>diminished</u>.

III+ has a major 3rd and an augmented 5th and is <u>augmented</u>. ('+' signifies augmented.)

Play the triads above to hear their sound. Then practise playing this exercise.

Comparing major with minor keys, observe these points.

(i) Triad types which are the same in both major and minor are V and vii°.

(ii) In major keys, I and IV are major; in minor keys, i and iv are minor. This reflects the tonality.

(iii) Major keys have **one** diminished triad vii°, minor keys have **two**, ii° and vii°.

(iv) There is only **one** augmented triad III+, and this is found in minor keys only.

■ Learn The pattern of triad types in minor keys is :
Minor Diminished Augmented Minor Major Major Diminished

Exercise 24 All triads in each line belong to the same minor key. For each triad write its root name, type and its roman numeral.

(a)

Triad name *supertonic*

Triad type *diminished*

Numeral ii°

(b)

Triad name

Triad type

Numeral

(c)

Triad name

Triad type

Numeral

THE PERFECT CADENCE

- As language is broken into phrases and sentences by the use of punctuation marks, so, too, music is divided into phrases and longer sections for easier understanding. At each phrase or section ending there is the sense of a cadence. A **cadence** is a musical punctuation mark. This effect of musical punctuation is enhanced by certain chord progressions. A **chord progression** is the sound of one chord linking to another.

A full stop in musical terms is called a **perfect cadence**, and as you might expect it has a strong, definite sound. This effect is made at a phrase ending when the dominant chord (V) is followed by the tonic (I).

This is a tune that everyone knows - *Happy Birthday.* It has 2 perfect cadences. The first is at the halfway point; the second at the end. Sing it and play along on the piano. Listen carefully to the perfect cadences.

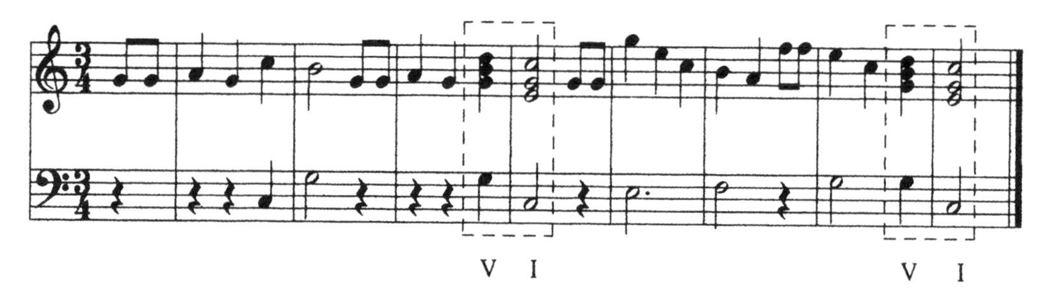

Notice how the cadences occur over a bar line. This is the normal rhythm of a cadence, allowing the stress to fall on the second chord.

Writing a perfect cadence for voices Note the following points:

1 The bass voice sings the 2 most important notes, i.e. the root of each chord.

These examples show perfect cadences in C major and A minor.

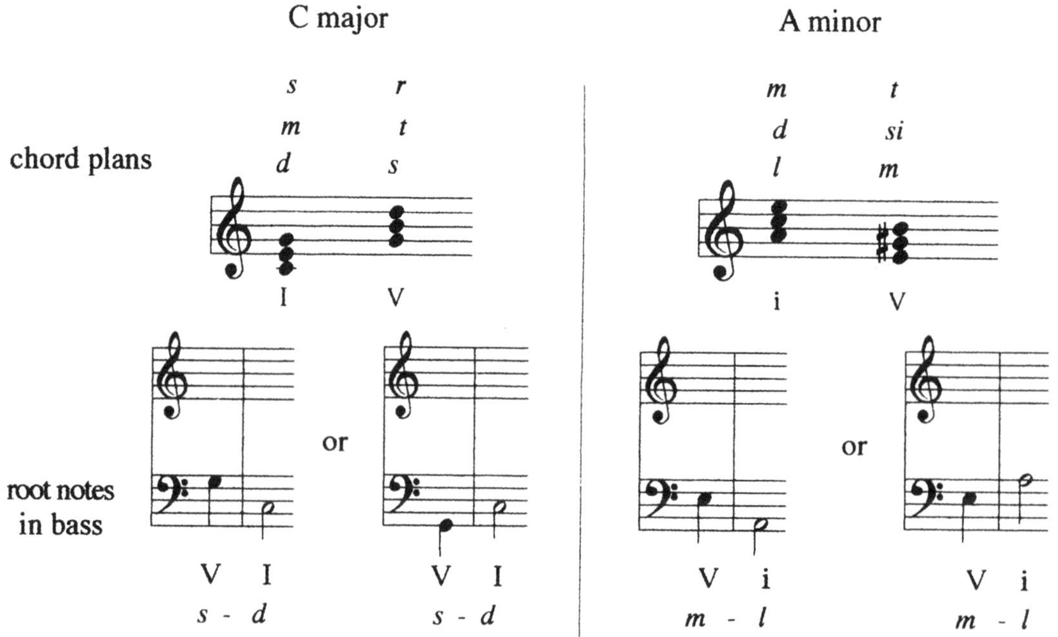

2 In simple vocal writing, the upper voices, i.e. soprano, alto and tenor mostly sing easy melodic lines - this means linking the chord notes as smoothly as possible.

The smoothest link for upper voices is the following:

The soprano may sing any of these melodic shapes. Then keeping range and spacing in mind, the alto and tenor will fill in the remaining parts.

■ The melodic shape created by each voice is called **part writing**.

Exercises 25 For each of the following exercises write a chord plan. Then complete these perfect cadences by adding parts for alto and tenor.

Exercise 25 continued.

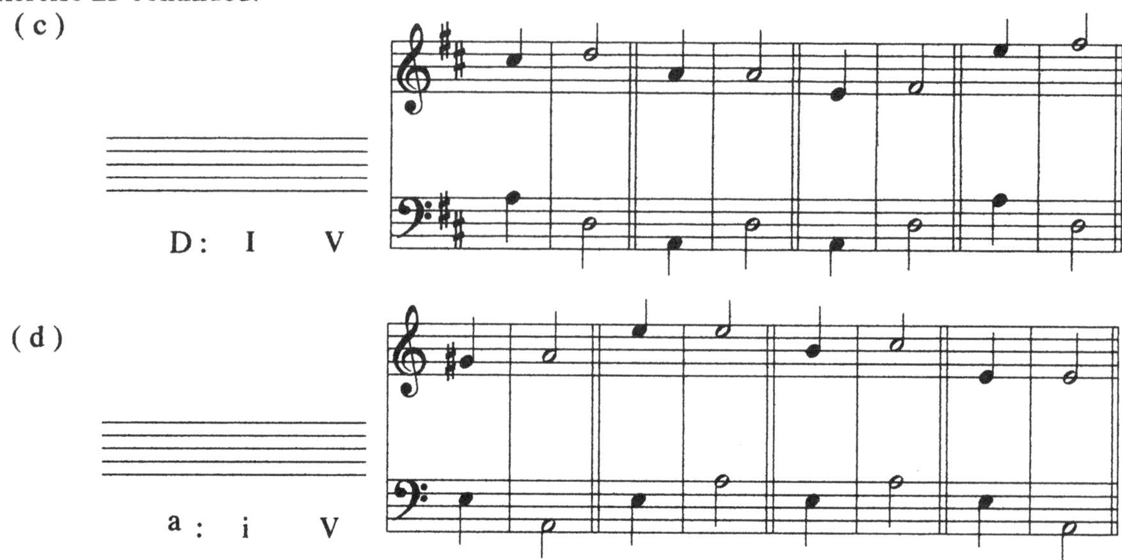

Exercise 26 In each of the following, complete the chord plan. Above the given bass notes add a soprano part. Then add parts for alto and tenor to make a perfect cadence.

Exercise 27 In each of the following, give the chord plan. In the bass write the root of each chord to form a perfect cadence. Add alto and tenor parts.

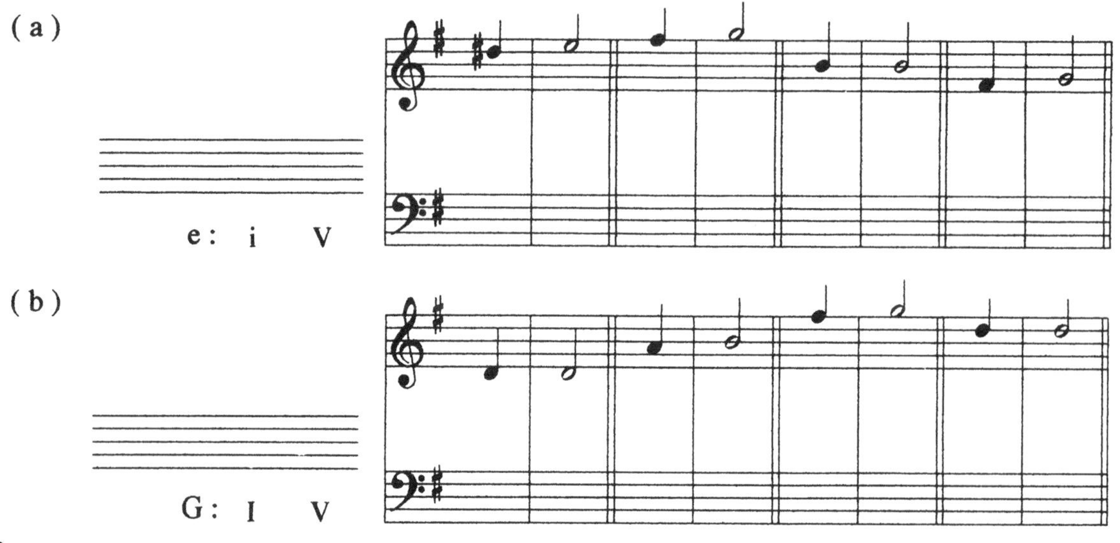

Exercise 28 These are phrase endings of folk songs harmonised by perfect cadences. Using the first as a guide, i) add the key name; ii) prepare a chord plan; iii) write solfa names over the last two melody notes; (iv) write numerals below the two bass notes.

Exercise 29 For each phrase i) name the key; ii) make a chord plan; iii) write solfa names above the bracketed melody notes; iv) write suitable bass notes only to make a perfect cadence, adding roman numerals.

■ NB The bass notes must have the same values as the melody notes above them.

THE IMPERFECT CADENCE

- An imperfect cadence is like a musical 'comma'. It occurs at a phrase ending which sounds unfinished. An imperfect cadence makes its effect when the phrase finishes on the dominant chord instead of on the tonic. The most common progression is I - V, so this will be studied first.

Looking again at the first two phrases of *Happy Birthday,* we see an imperfect cadence at the end of the first phrase. Play and sing the tune and listen now for the different effects made by the imperfect and perfect cadences.

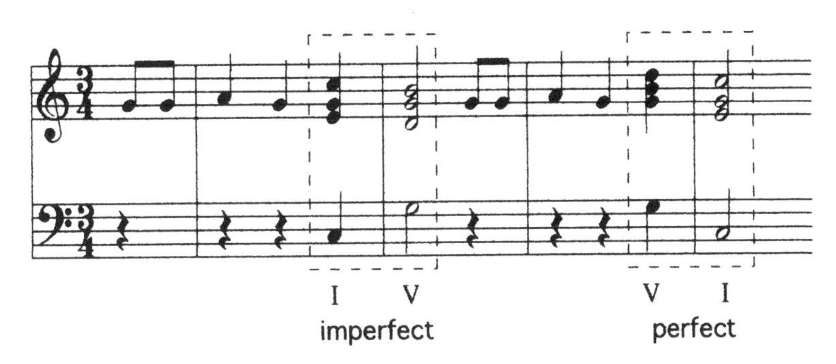

Writing an imperfect cadence for voices First, put the root of each chord in the bass.

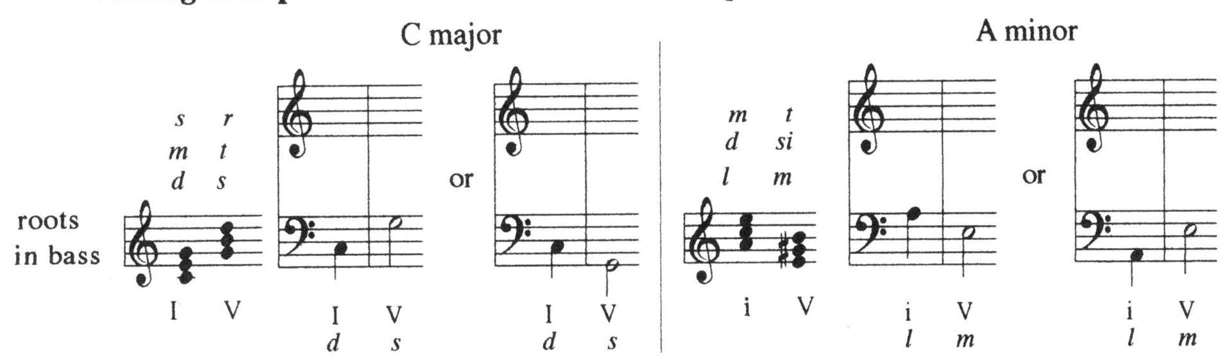

Part writing The smoothest link for upper voices is the following.

Exercise 30 Write a chord plan. Add parts for alto and tenor to make imperfect cadences.

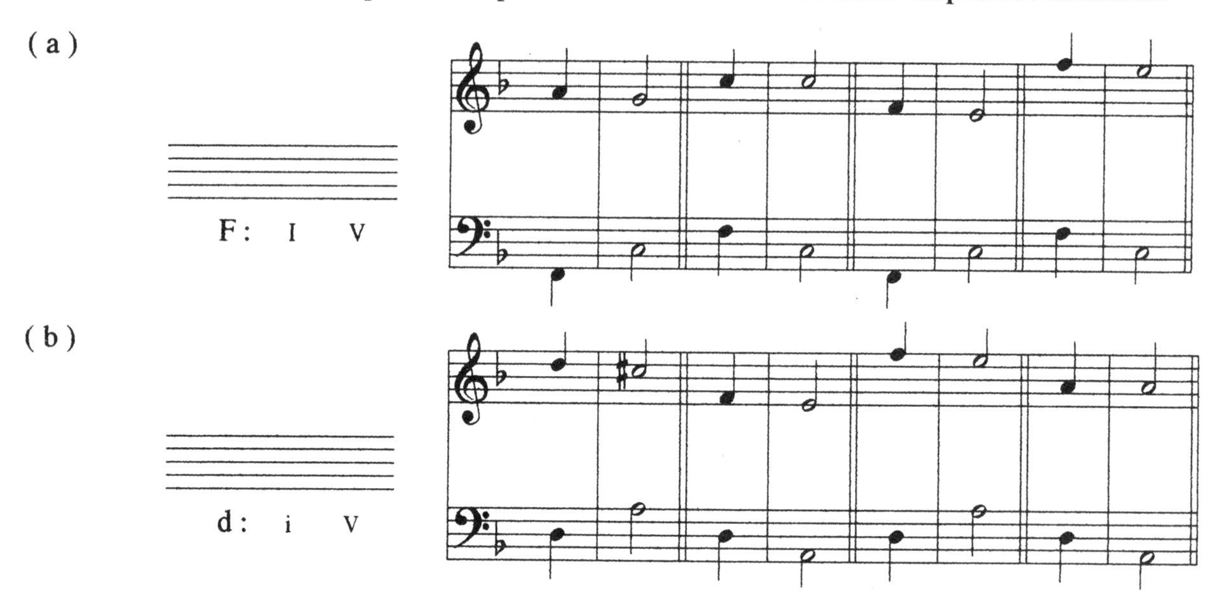

Exercise 31 Write a chord plan. Add soprano, alto and tenor parts to make imperfect cadences.

Exercise 32 To these soprano parts, add bass, alto and tenor parts to make imperfect cadences.

Exercise 33 Each phrase ending has been harmonised by a perfect or imperfect cadence. For each line of music, follow this order of work.

i) Identify the key.
ii) Make a chord plan.
iii) Write solfa names above the bracketed melody notes.
iv) Write roman numerals and cadence names.

(a)

solfa names

Key ____

numerals ____ ____

cadence name ____ ____

(b)

solfa names

etc.

Key ____

numerals ____ ____

cadence name ____ ____

(c)

solfa names

Key ____

numerals ____ ____

cadence name ____ ____

(d)

solfa names

Key ____

numerals ____ ____

cadence name ____ ____

Exercise 34 Harmonise each phrase ending with a perfect or imperfect cadence. For each line of music follow this order of work.

i) Identify the key.
ii) Make a chord plan.
iii) Write solfa names above the last 2 notes of each phrase. These are bracketed.
iv) Write numerals and suitable bass notes to end each phrase.
v) Give cadence names.

(a)

solfa names

etc.

Key ____

numerals ______ ______

cadence name ______________ ______________

(b)

solfa names

Key ____

numerals ______ ______

cadence name ______________ ______________

(c)

solfa names

Key ____

numerals ______ ______

cadence name ______________ ______________

(d)

solfa names

etc.

Key ____

numerals ______ ______

cadence name ______________ ______________

MELODY WRITING over TONIC and DOMINANT CHORDS

- **Use of Chords** When music is analysed, it is often surprising how much use is made of the tonic and dominant chords, not only at cadences but as building blocks within the phrases. This piano piece by Schumann, *The Wild Horseman,* is a good example. It is almost entirely built on tonic and dominant chords. Play and listen to the piece while you follow the chord analysis below. All chords are tonic or dominant except those marked * .

- **Melody** One of the most important aspects of harmony is its melodic interest. This varies a good deal depending on the style and medium for which it is written, e.g. whether for voice or an instrument. In a hymn tune, as a rule, each melody note is accompanied by a separate chord. In a folk-song the tune is the main interest so chords are used sparingly. In instrumental writing the melodic shapes will tend to use a much wider range of pitch than is common in vocal music. It is also easier to play fast, complex rhythms on an instrument than it is to sing them.

To create a simple melody line over a single chord consider the following points.

- **Rhythm** For interest, it is likely that the rhythm of the melody will be more 'active' than the bass, e.g.

Rhythm of melody	♩ ♩ ♩	or	♩. ♪ ♩	or	♫ ♫ ♩
Rhythm of bass :	𝅗𝅥.		𝅗𝅥.		𝅗𝅥.

- **Melodic Shape** This can be achieved in a number of ways.

1 The simplest is to use the chord notes in an arpeggio shape. Here are arpeggio shapes using the notes of chord I in C major.

2 For a smoother melodic shape chord notes may be linked by 'passing notes'. A **passing note** is not part of a chord but forms a 'stepping stone' between chord notes which are a 3rd apart. In these examples, the added passing notes are marked * .

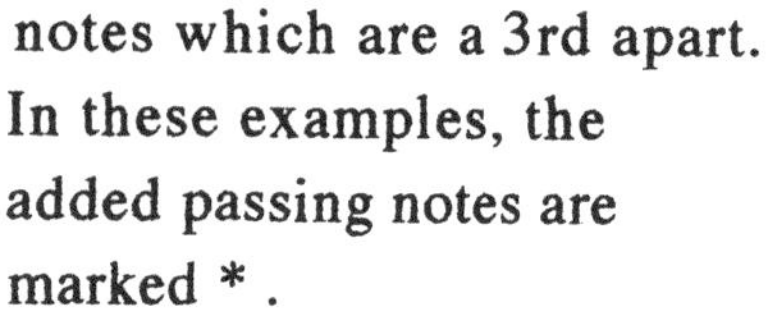

■ Passing notes are usually weak quavers. This is the case in the examples above.

Quaver 1 of a pair is 'on the beat' and is therefore <u>strong</u>.
Quaver 2 of a pair is 'off the beat' and is therefore <u>weak</u>.
A passing note is sometimes a <u>weak-beat</u> crotchet as here.

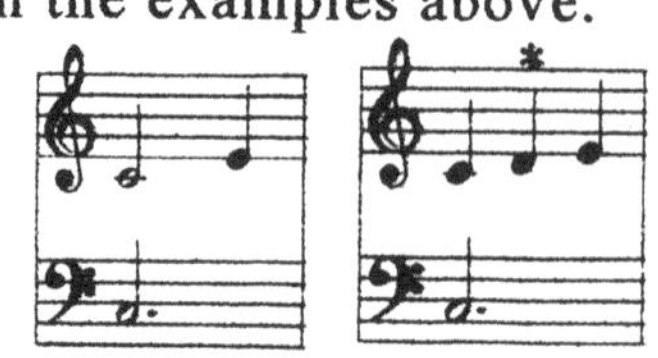

A melody may be created in a similar way on chord V. These examples are in C major.

Exercise 35 Write arpeggio shapes in the treble above each given base root.

Exercise 36 Rewrite the melody shapes with passing notes. Add numerals below the bass.

Exercise 37 Listen to this simple piece. Then do the exercises which follow it.

i) Complete the chord plan. Write a numeral below each bass root.

ii) Circle all passing notes.

iii) Name the cadence used to end each phrase. ______________ ______________

Melody in a Minor Key In a minor key, writing a melody on chords i and V is basically the same. However, take special care with chord V when adding passing notes. Chord V = *m - si - t*. The 'stepping stone' or passing note between *m* and *si* will be *fi* . (*f* would make an awkward augmented 2nd interval with *si*.)

Study the following examples in A minor. The added passing notes are marked *.

Exercise 38 Add a numeral below each bass root and write arpeggio shapes in the treble.

Exercise 39 Re-write each melodic shape to include passing notes. Add a numeral below each bass root.

Exercise 40 Listen to this piece.Then do these exercises.

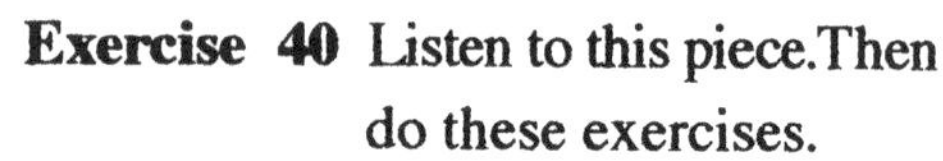

a Make a chord plan.

b Write a numeral below each bass root.

c Circle all passing notes.

d Name the cadence used to end the first phrase. ______________

e What type of cadence is used at the end of the piece? ______________

- **Longer Melodies** You are now ready to write a longer melody above a bass which combines chords I and V. The most important thing is to make a smooth link in the melody on the beat where the chord changes. This allows the melody to move logically to the new group of sounds. Look at pages 27 and 31 to see the smoothest links between these chords. Listen to this piece in G major - it uses chords I and V.

Notice the smooth melodic link where the chord changes occur, i.e. the end of bar 1 to the beginning of bar 2, and the end of bar 3 to the beginning of bar 4.

Exercise 41 Complete each chord plan, adding numerals below the bass roots. Continue each tune from the given opening. When finished writing, play each completed piece.

THE PLAGAL CADENCE

● You have learnt how to create the effect of a full stop at the end of a phrase or section by using the dominant chord followed by the tonic. This is the perfect cadence. Another way of creating the effect of a full stop is to use the subdominant chord followed by the tonic. This is the **plagal cadence**. You will recognise its sound if you think of the *Amen* at the end of a hymn. It is little used apart from this;-□ it occurs occasionally in folk songs.

The chorus of *'We Three Kings of Orient are'* gives a rare example of several plagal cadences in the same melody. Note them as you listen to the extract.

Writing a plagal cadence for voices First, put the root of each chord in the bass.

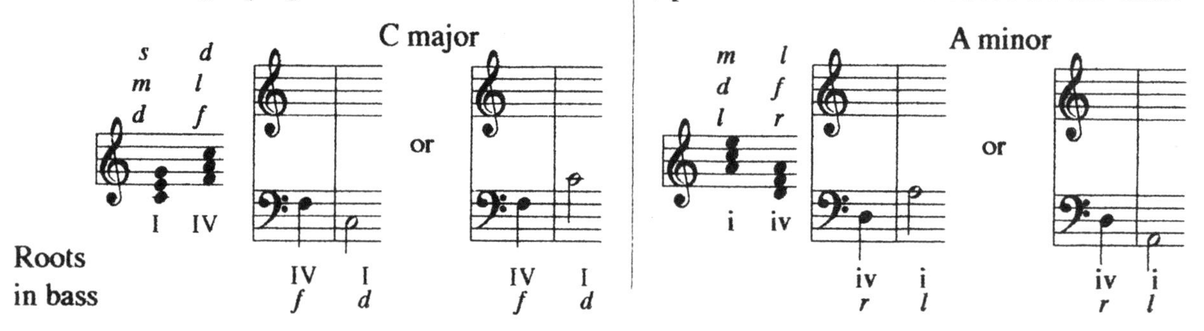

Part writing The smoothest link for upper voices is the following:

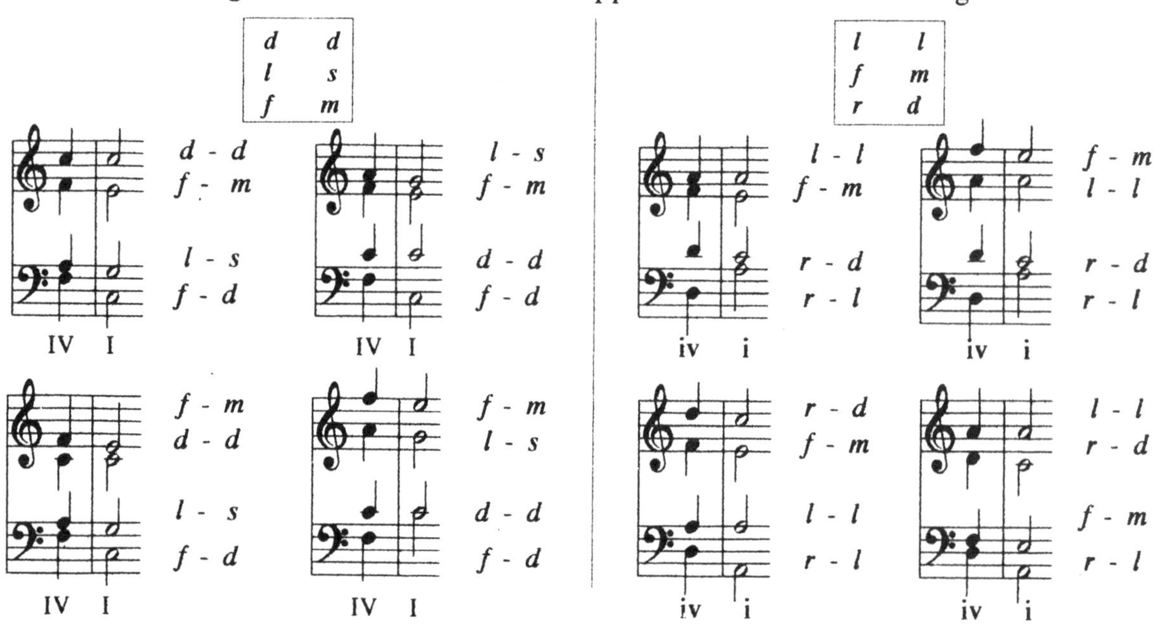

Exercise 42 Complete the chord plan. Then add alto and tenor parts to form plagal cadences.

Exercise 43 Finish the plan. Add soprano, alto and tenor parts to form plagal cadences.

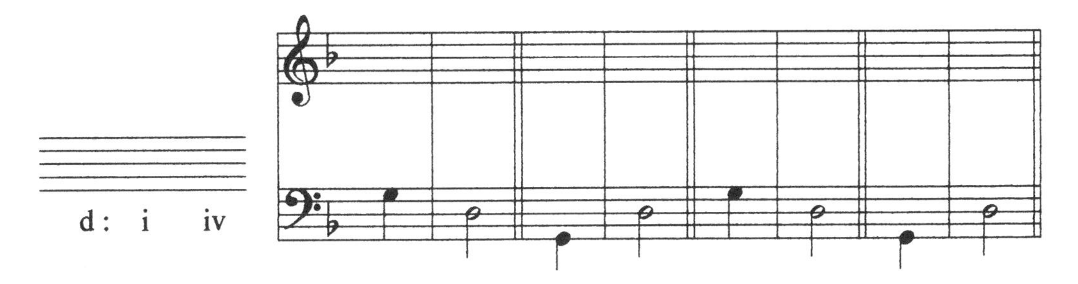

Exercise 44 Finish the plan. Add a bass part, then alto and tenor parts to form plagal cadences.

Exercise 45 These are the bass parts of perfect, imperfect or plagal cadences. Finish each chord plan. Add numerals, then soprano, alto and tenor parts. Give cadence names.

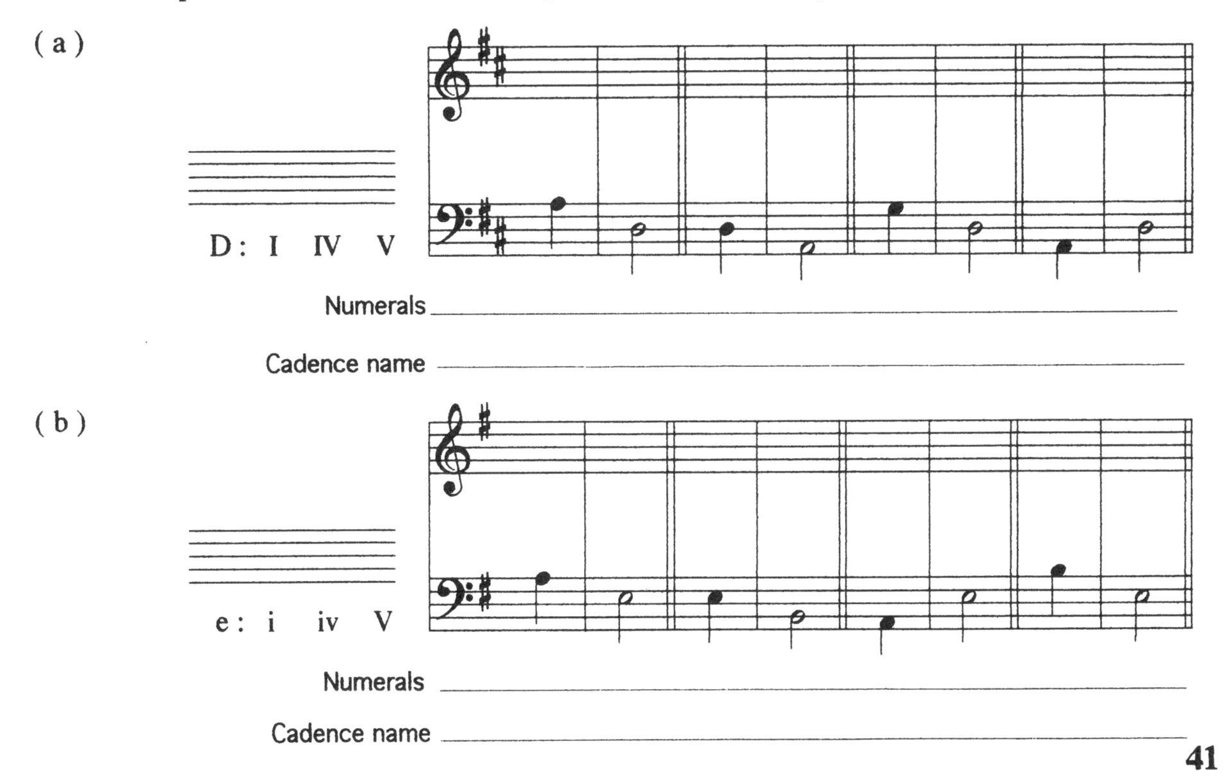

Exercise 46 Each phrase ending is harmonised by a perfect, imperfect or plagal cadence.

i) Identify the key.

ii) Make a chord plan.

iii) Write solfa names above the bracketed melody notes.

iv) Write roman numerals and cadence names.

■ Cadences can occur other than across a bar line; see (a), (c) and (d) marked *: but the chords should normally move from a weak beat to a strong beat.

Exercise 47 Harmonise each phrase ending with a perfect, imperfect or plagal cadence.

i) Identify the key.
ii) Make a chord plan.
iii) Write solfa names above the last 2 notes of each phrase. These are bracketed.
iv) Write numerals and suitable bass notes for each phrase ending.
v) Add cadence names.

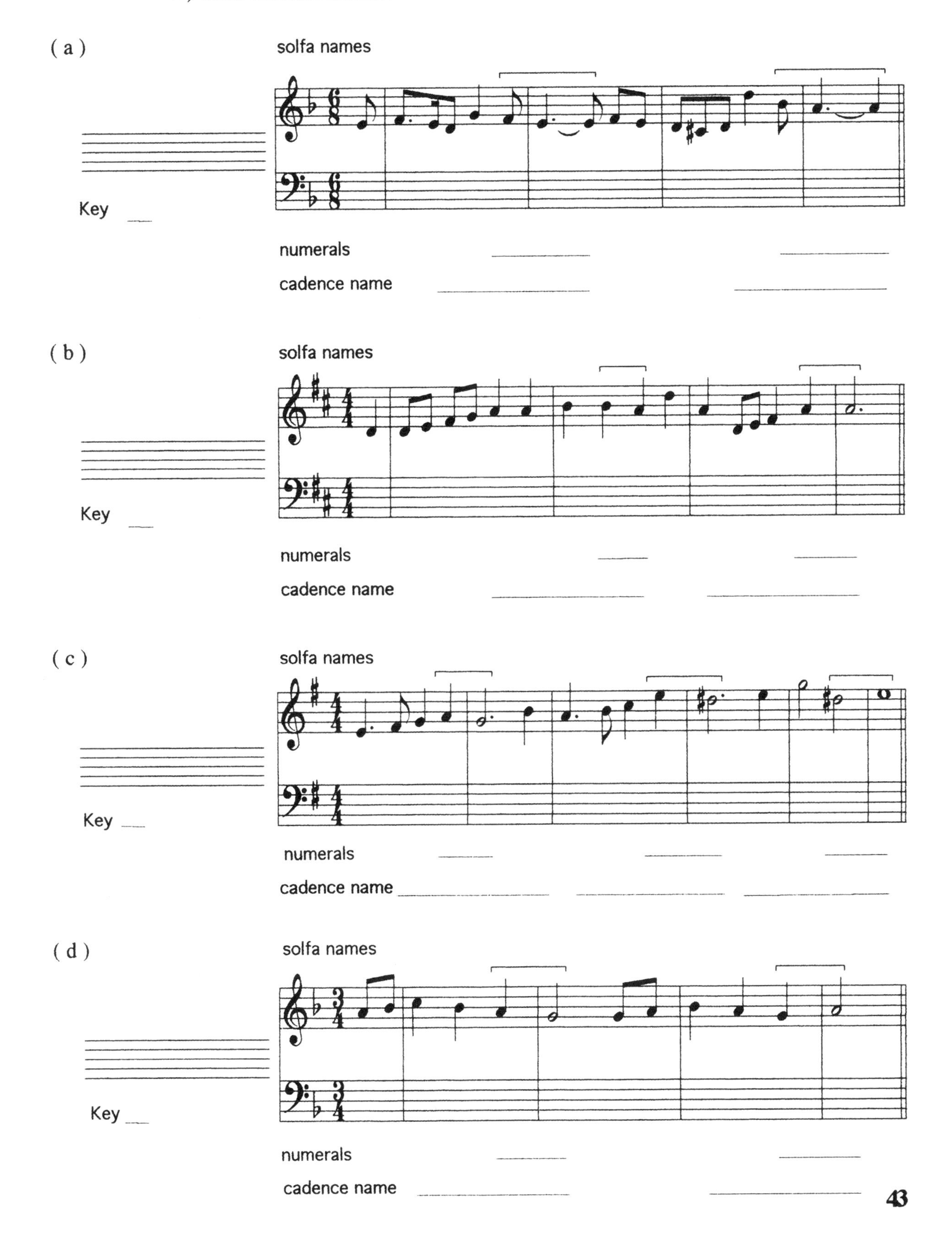

MORE on PART WRITING

- So far, part writing for the upper voices has been kept as smooth as possible at chord changes, i.e. either moving by step or repeating a note. However, this is not the only possibility for good part writing. When writing root position progressions, any upper voice may move a 3rd and still make a smooth enough melodic link to the next chord. Study these examples in C major.

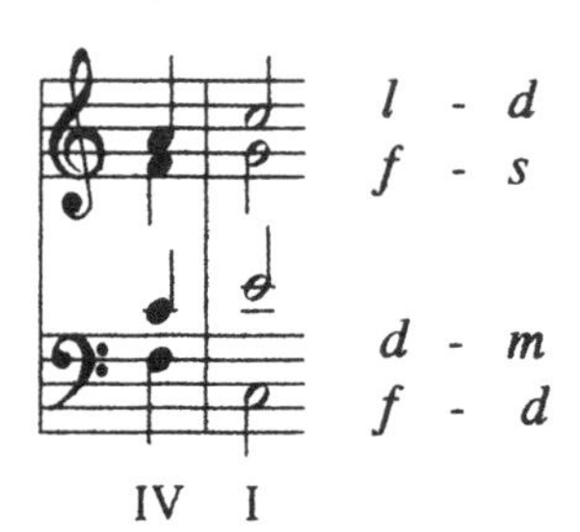

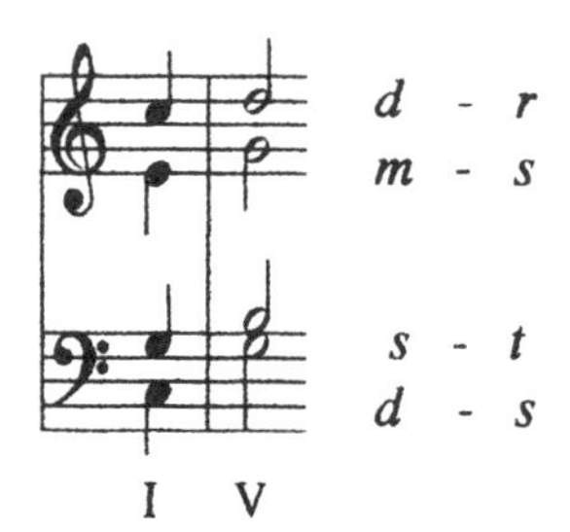

C major | A minor

Part Writing and the Leading Note

Treat the leading note very sensitively. It has a naturally strong pull to the tonic as the chord changes. This is especially important when it is part of the main melody line, i.e. in the soprano part.

Part writing - a special case

It is common for melodies to end *r - d* (*t - l* minor) in a perfect cadence. But this poses a question for inner part writing as shown.
See the solutions suggested below.

Special Case - Solution 1

Because the leading note is in an inner part, and therefore less obvious, it may fall a 3rd. (Bach favours this solution.)

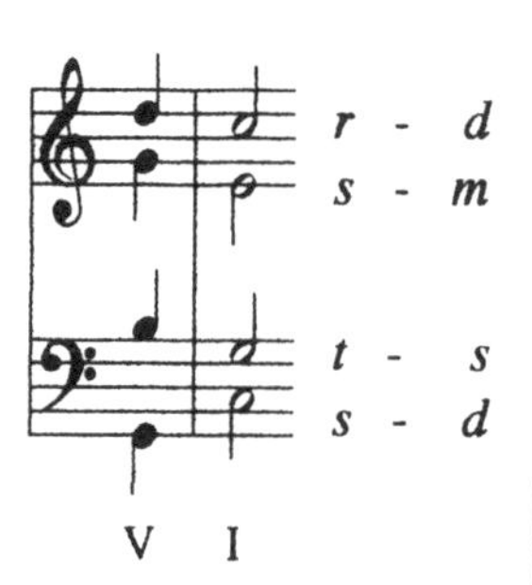

Special Case - Solution 2

Let the leading note rise to the tonic as usual. This produces three roots and no 5th in the final chord. (The 5th is the least important note of the triad and can therefore be omitted.)

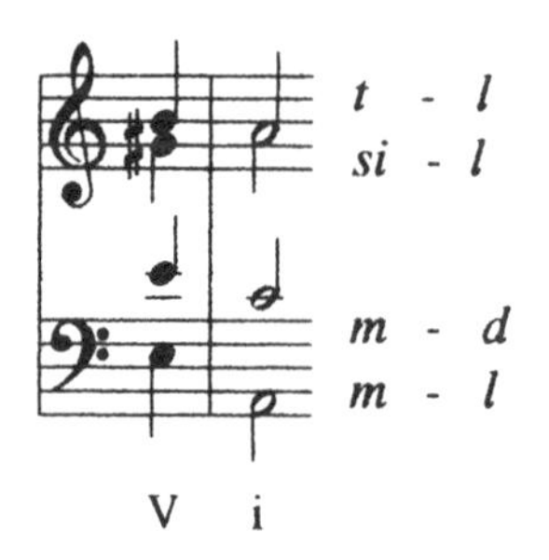

Exercise 48 Each exercise includes an imperfect, a plagal and two perfect cadences. For each exercise, make a chord plan and add numerals below the bass. Add alto and tenor parts and a cadence name.

MELODY WRITING over TONIC and SUBDOMINANT CHORDS

- **Chords** As well as making a plagal cadence at a phrase ending, subdominant and tonic chords make good harmony partners. Either combination of these chords (IV - I and I - IV) creates a natural sounding progression and makes useful building blocks within a phrase. These progressions can be heard in the following short extracts from piano pieces by Schumann.

- **Melody** Arpeggio shapes may be used to create a melody as before. Passing notes may also be included as stepping stones between chord notes for a smoother shape. These are some examples using the notes of chord IV in C major. Added passing notes are marked * .

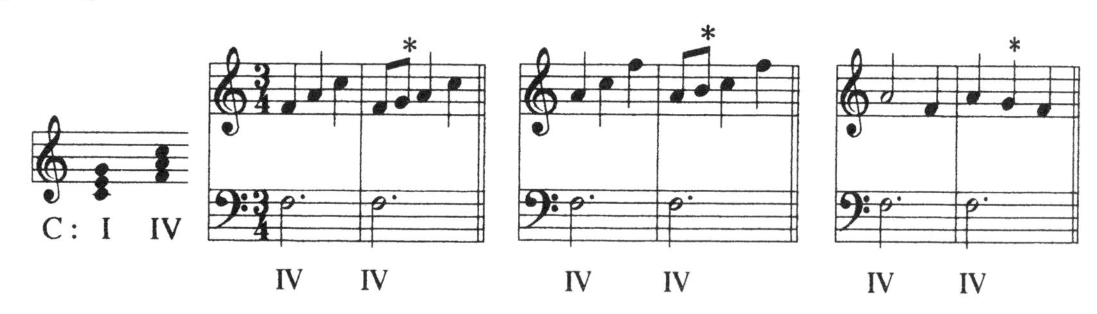

- **Minor Key** Take care when adding passing notes on chord iv in a minor key. Chord iv = *r f l*. The passing note which links *f* and *l* will be *s*. (*Si* would make an awkward augmented 2nd interval with *f*.) Study these examples which are in A minor.

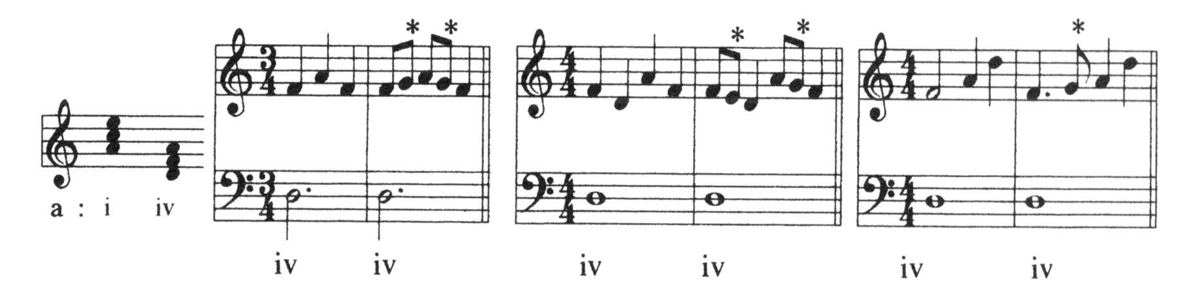

Exercise 49 Finish each plan and add numerals below the bass roots. Continue each melody from the given opening. When finished, play each completed piece.
■ Remember to link notes smoothly at a chord change.

MELODY WRITING over a GIVEN BASS : AUXILIARY NOTES

- **Auxiliary notes** You learnt how chord notes form the framework of a melody over a given bass. Passing notes are then added to give a smooth stepwise link between pairs of chord notes. Decoration may also be added in the form of 'auxiliary notes'. An **auxiliary note** moves between repeated chord notes and may be either a step higher or lower. Study these examples in C major. The auxiliary notes are marked * .

Auxiliary notes, like passing notes, are weak quavers usually. An auxiliary note can also be a weak-beat crotchet as in the last example.

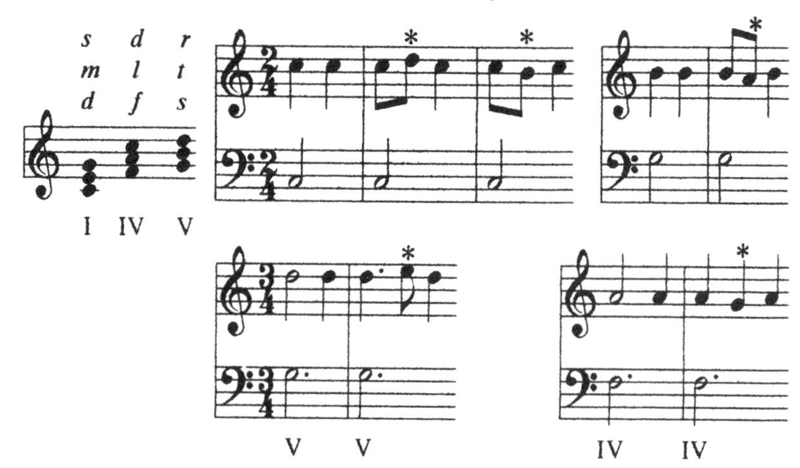

Minor key Take care in the minor key when adding an auxiliary note below *si* in chord V. The auxiliary note will be *fi*. (*f* would make an augmented 2nd with *si*.) Similar care is needed when adding an auxiliary note above *f* in chord iv. The auxiliary note will be *s*. (*Si* would make an augmented 2nd with *f*.) In other words, the passing or auxiliary note should 'agree' with the chord note which it decorates.

Chord note *si* (ch V) : decorative note = *fi*	Chord note *f* (ch iv) : decorative note = *s*

In this simple piece in G major, Example 1 shows the framework of the melody using only chord notes. Play it and compare it with Example 2 which includes passing and auxiliary notes to create a more flowing melodic shape.
Note: passing notes are marked P ; auxiliary notes are marked A.

Passing notes included so far were between notes of the same chord. But passing notes may be added between any two chord notes a 3rd apart, whether or not they belong to the same chord. The passing note which is included at * in example 2 links notes of different chords.

Exercise 50 The framework of each melody shows only chord notes. For each write a chord plan and add numerals. Continue from the given opening to decorate each melody by adding suitable passing and auxiliary notes.

Exercise 50 continued

Exercise 51 Complete each chord plan and add numerals below the bass roots. Continue each melody from the given opening. When you have finished writing, play each completed piece.

AN IMPERFECT CADENCE using IV - V

- An imperfect cadence is heard when a phrase ends on the dominant chord. Different chords may approach V at the cadence. I -V has been studied; now IV - V is discussed. Listen to this extract in C major which ends with an imperfect cadence using IV - V.

Play the examples below which show different part writing for IV - V in C major.

Having listened, which makes a more 'rounded' sound **a** or **b** ? It is **b**. Example **a** is more brassy or strident because we hear two 5ths in a row(S and A). Also two 8ves are heard in a row (B and A).

consecutive 5ths

consecutive 8ves

The 'open' sound made by these consecutive intervals is sometimes heard in modern vocal writing but it is not part of a more conventional style. It is easy to avoid consecutive 5ths and octaves if you do as in **b** , i.e. as the bass rises, all upper voices move down.

Summary of part-writing for voices

The smoothest downward link for upper voices is

d - t	l - si
l - s	f - m
f - r	r - t

Exercise 52 Finish the chord plan; add alto and tenor parts to form imperfect cadences.

Exercise 53 Finish the plan; add soprano, alto and tenor parts to form imperfect cadences.

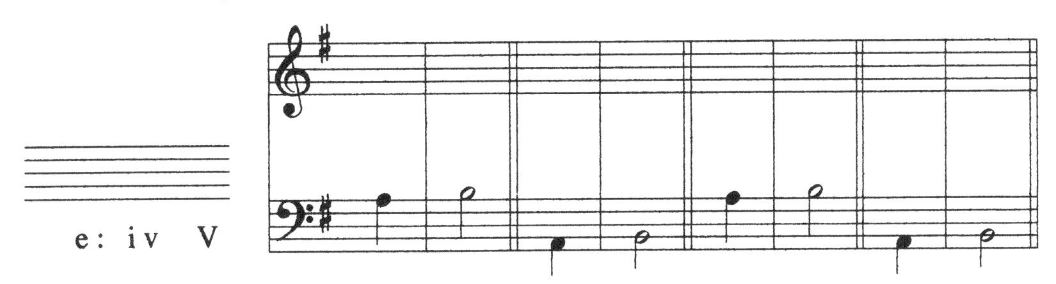

Exercise 54 Finish the plan; add bass, alto and tenor parts to form imperfect cadences.

Exercise 55 These are the bass parts of perfect, imperfect or plagal cadences. Complete each chord plan and write numerals below the bass. Add soprano, alto and tenor parts and a cadence name.

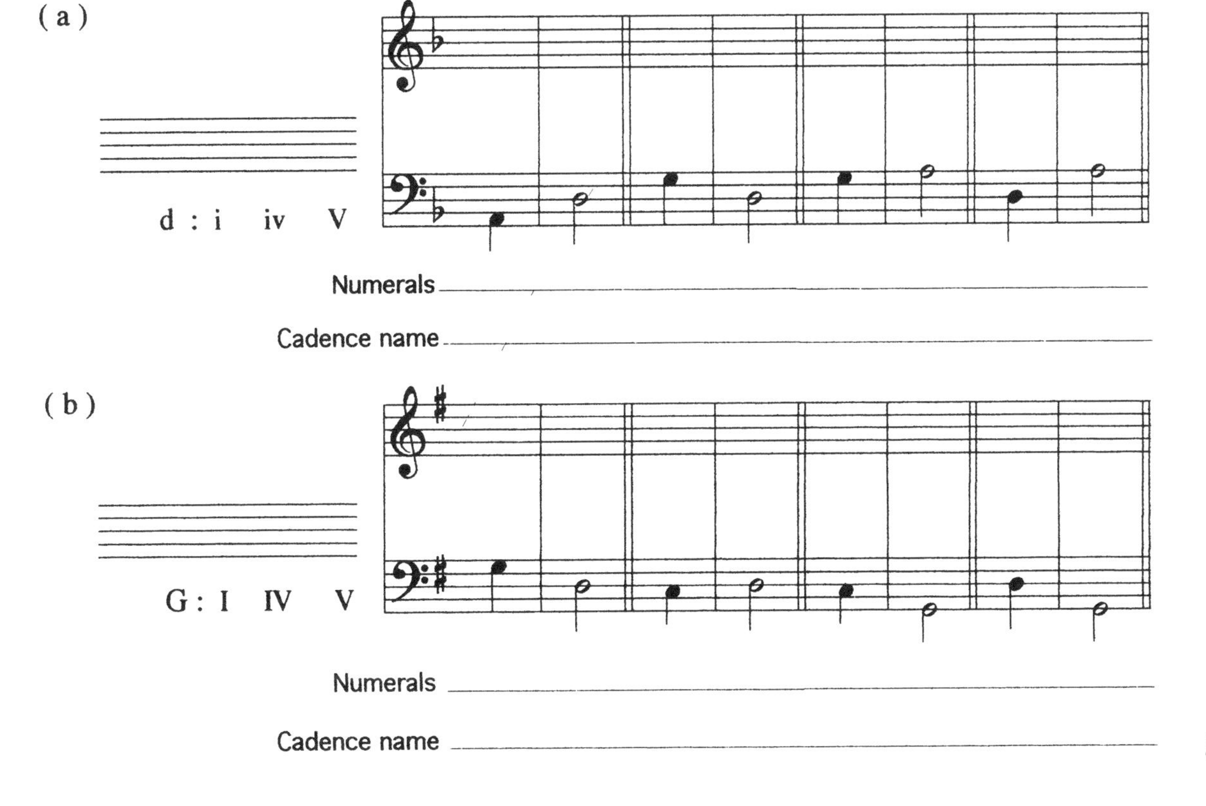

Exercise 56 Each phrase ending is harmonised by a perfect, imperfect or plagal cadence.

i) Name the key.
ii) Make a chord plan.
iii) Write solfa names above the bracketed melody notes.
iv) Write roman numerals and a cadence name under each cadence.

Exercise 57 Each of these melodies has four short phrases. Harmonise the bracketed phrase endings, making perfect, imperfect or plagal cadences. Add chord plans, solfa names, numerals and cadence names.

N.B. Each melody is to contain an example of each progression learnt so far: (I - V, IV - V, V - I, IV - I) and should end with a final cadence which is perfect or plagal.

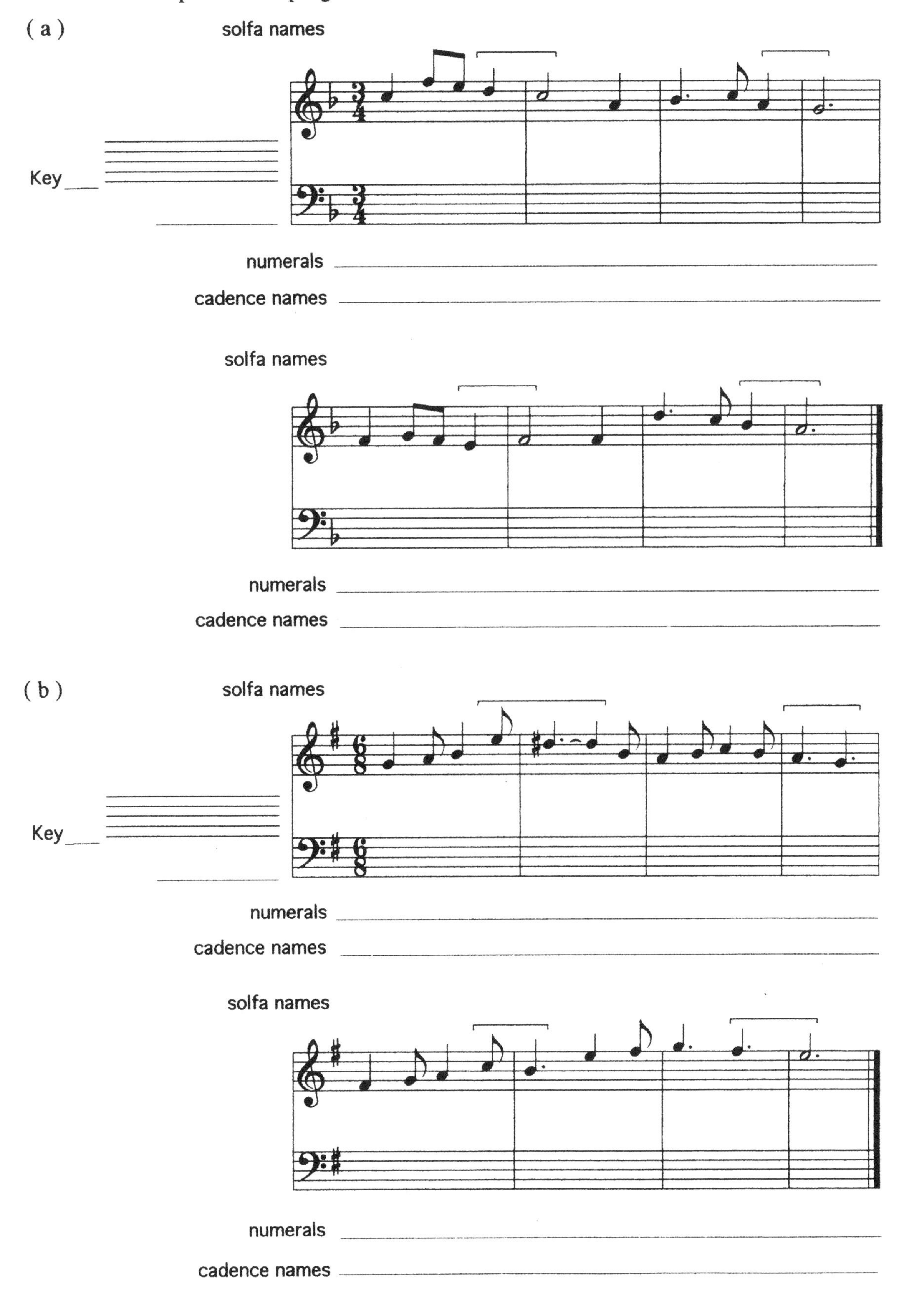

ANOTHER IMPERFECT CADENCE : ii - V major keys

- In a major key chord ii = *r f l* which is a minor chord .
  In a minor key chord ii = *t r f* which is a diminished chord.

Simple harmony makes most use of major and minor chords. Diminished chords, though also useful, need careful treatment and will be discussed in the next grade. So, for the present, chord ii will only be included in major keys.

At a phrase ending, ii - V is another form of imperfect cadence. Listen to this simple piano arrangement of "*Here we go round the mulberry bush*". The phrase finishes with an imperfect cadence using chords ii - V.

Part -writing for voices

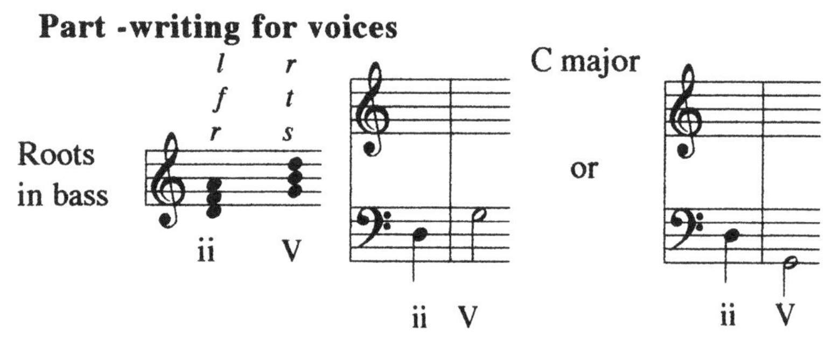

A smooth link for upper voices has two possibilities.

Exercise 58 Make a chord plan; then add alto and tenor parts using possibility 1 above.

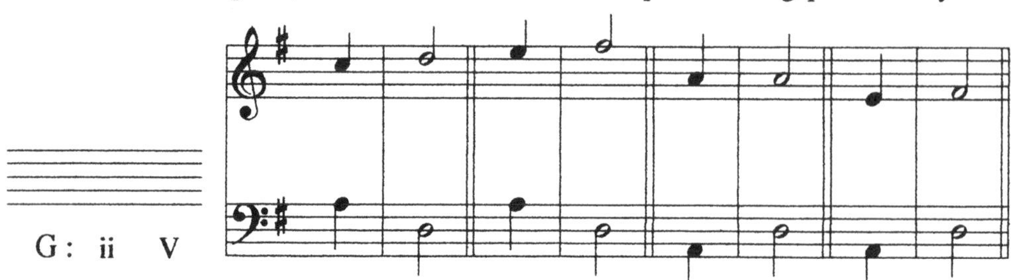

Exercise 59 Complete the chord plan. Then add alto and tenor parts using possibility 2.

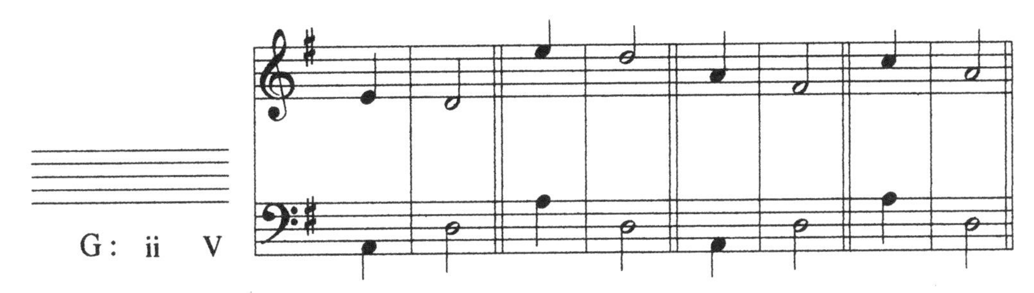

Exercise 60 Complete the chord plan; add soprano, alto and tenor parts.

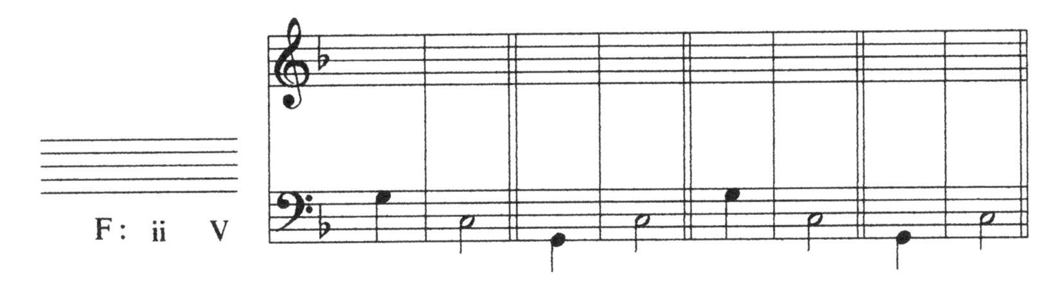

Exercise 61 Complete the chord plan; add bass, alto and tenor parts.

Exercise 62 The bass parts include 3 types of imperfect cadence (I - V, ii - V, IV - V). Finish each chord plan; add numerals. Write soprano, alto and tenor parts.

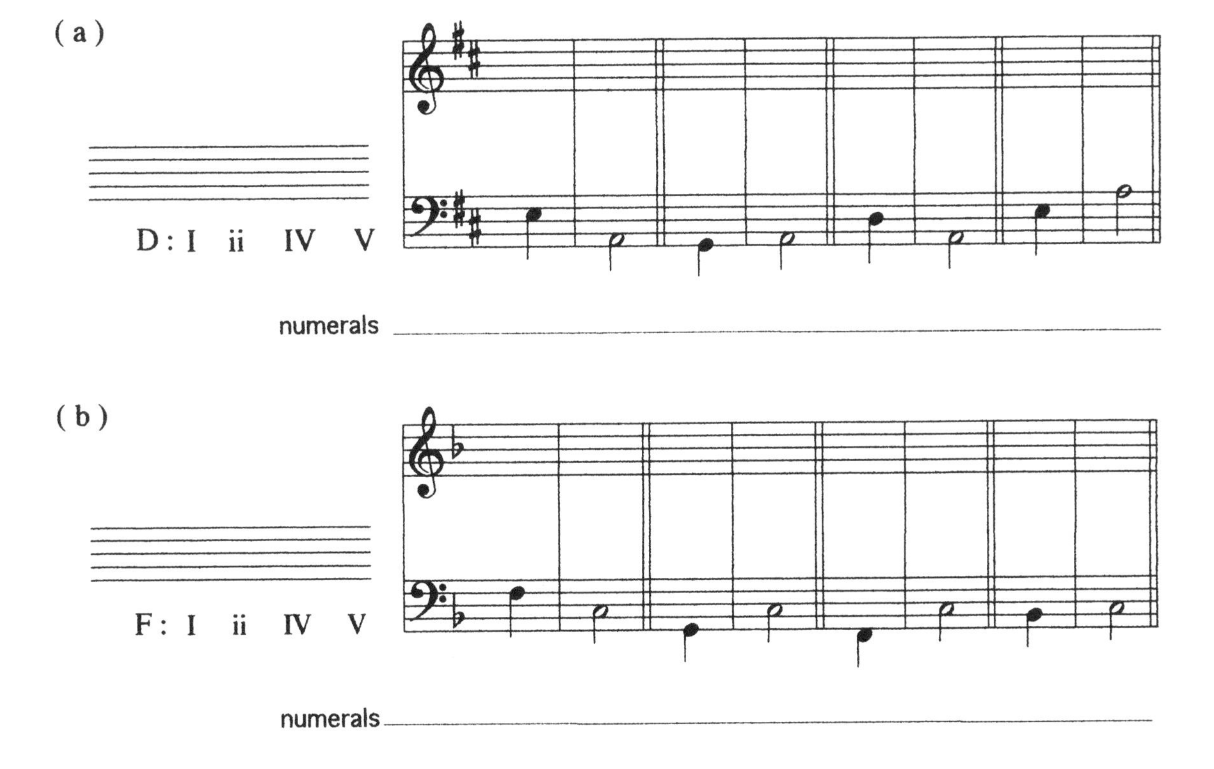

Exercise 63 Each melody has 5 short phrases. Harmonise the bracketed phrase endings, making perfect, imperfect or plagal cadences. Add chord plans, solfa names, roman numerals and cadence names.

Each melody is to contain an example of each progression learnt (I - V , ii - V , IV - V , V - I , IV - I) and should end with a final cadence which is perfect or plagal.

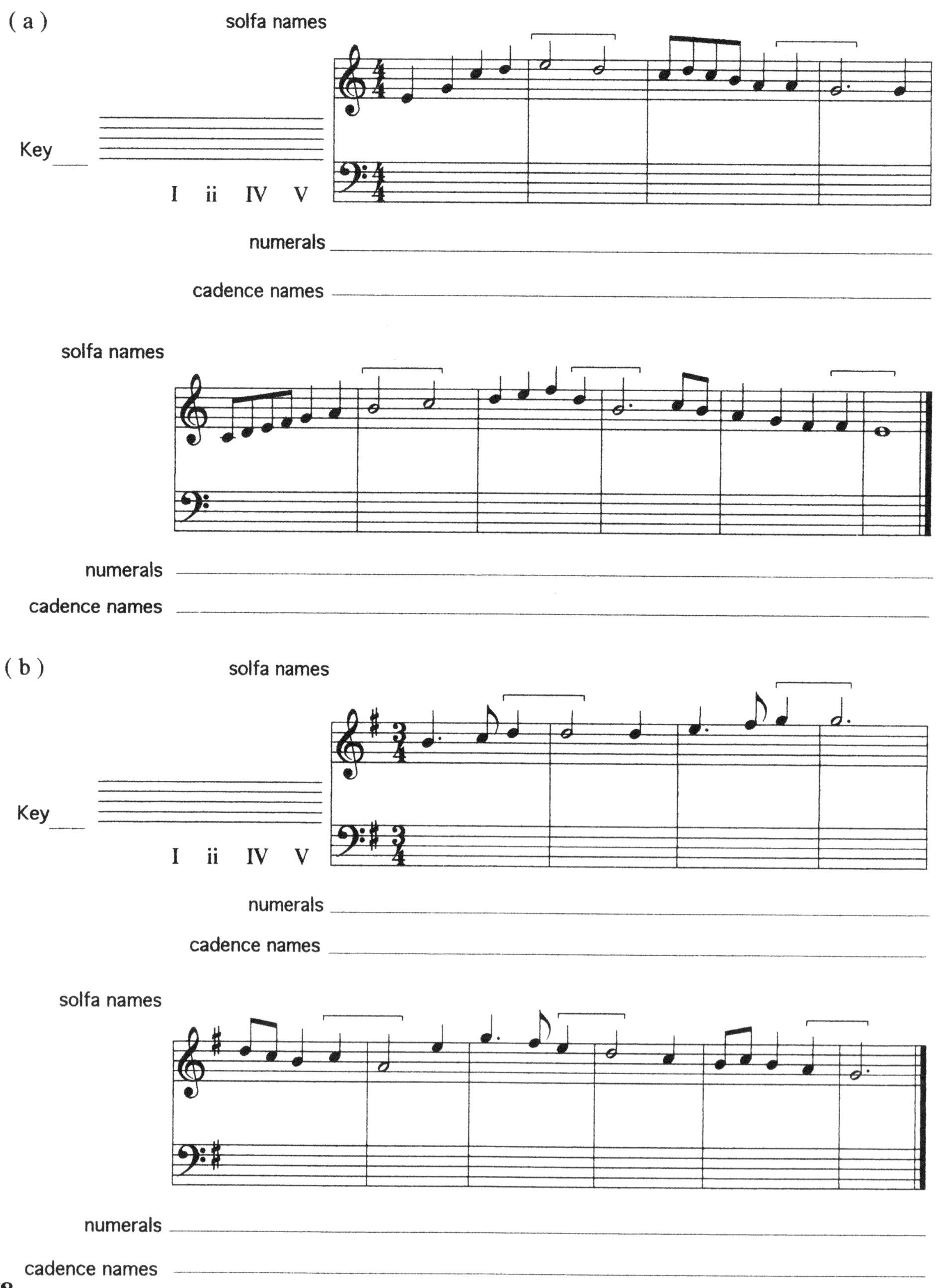

MELODY WRITING over a GIVEN BASS : CHORD ii MAJOR KEYS

- The given bass will now have several more progressions at its disposal, i.e. IV - V and ii - V , but the latter one in major keys only.

IV and ii also combine well as a lead up to Chord V , i.e. IV - ii - V or extended further to become IV - ii - V - I. Progressions will be studied in more detail in the next grade; for the moment they are decided for you in the given bass.

- Keep this summary of points in mind when melody writing.

1. Keep the melody simple enough to be singable.
2. Use chord notes to create a framework.
3. Make a smooth melodic link at all chord changes, i.e. not moving more than the interval of a 3rd.
4. Remember that downward movement is best for the melody over a IV - V progression. (This generally applies where the bass rises a step, as in I - ii.)
5. Finally decorate by including some passing notes and/or auxiliary notes.

Listen to Example A. Then read and study the points made about it.

Example A

(a) Notice the IV - V progression from bar 1 - 2. A downward-pointing arrow acts as a reminder for the direction of the melody over this progression.

(b) Listen carefully to the progression of chords in bars 3 and 4. This pattern of chords is very commonly used.

Example B

This is a decorated version of A. Listen, then study the further points made.

(c) Many passing notes have been added to link up the chord notes and so achieve a more flowing singable melody.

(d) Notice the auxiliary note marked * in bar 4. This note is included between repeated notes of <u>different</u> chords. An auxiliary note may be included between repeated notes whether or not the chord changes.

(e) The melody at the end of bar 2 has been left undecorated - the minim gives a sense of 'space' for the phrase ending.

Exercise 64 The framework of each melody shows only chord notes. For each, make a chord plan. Add numerals. Rewrite, adding passing and auxiliary notes where suitable.

Exercise 65 Complete the chord plans and add numerals below the bass roots. Continue each melody from the given opening. When you have finished writing, play each completed piece.

THE INTERRUPTED CADENCE V - VI

- There is an element of surprise in the sound of an interrupted cadence. This effect is heard when chord V is followed, not by chord I as is usual, but by chord VI.

Listen to this extract from the last section of Handel's *Largo*, It is printed here in a keyboard arrangement. Compare the effect of the interrupted cadence with the perfect cadence which follows it.

The last phrase is a repeat of the first, but now ends with a perfect cadence.

Writing an interrupted cadence for voices

Notice the bass shape in V - VI. It has a similar shape to that of IV - V, i.e. the roots rise a step. In part writing, if all the voices rise a step, the stylistic problem of consecutive 5ths and octaves will occur as in example (a).

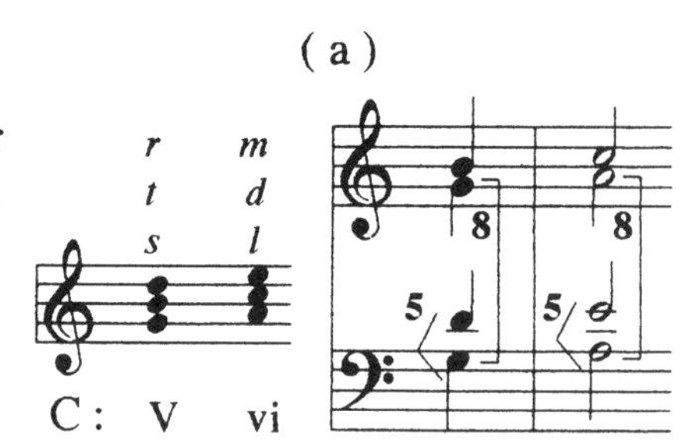

If all the upper voices move down, the problem of consecutive 5ths and octaves is solved. However, in doing so the leading note and its need to rise to the tonic is being overlooked as in this example.

The best part writing is shown in example (c). Here, the leading note rises to the tonic while the other upper voices fall. A result of this movement is that the 3rd is doubled in chord VI.

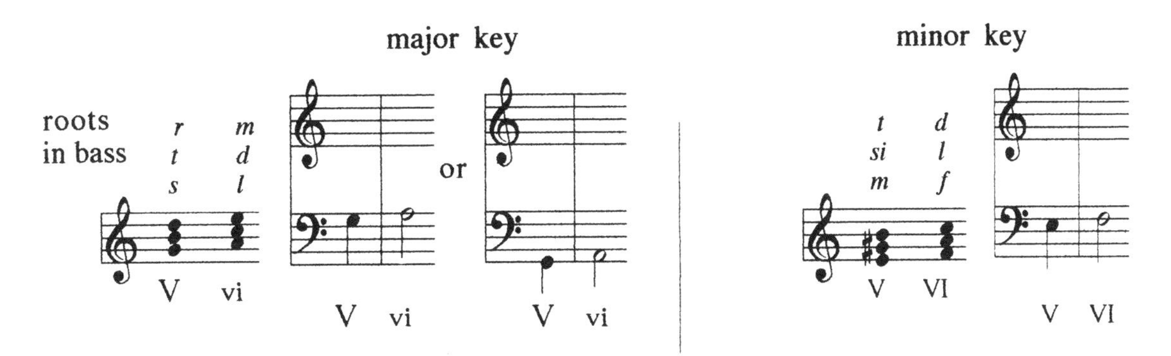

Part-writing The special link for upper voices is: leading note rises — other parts fall.

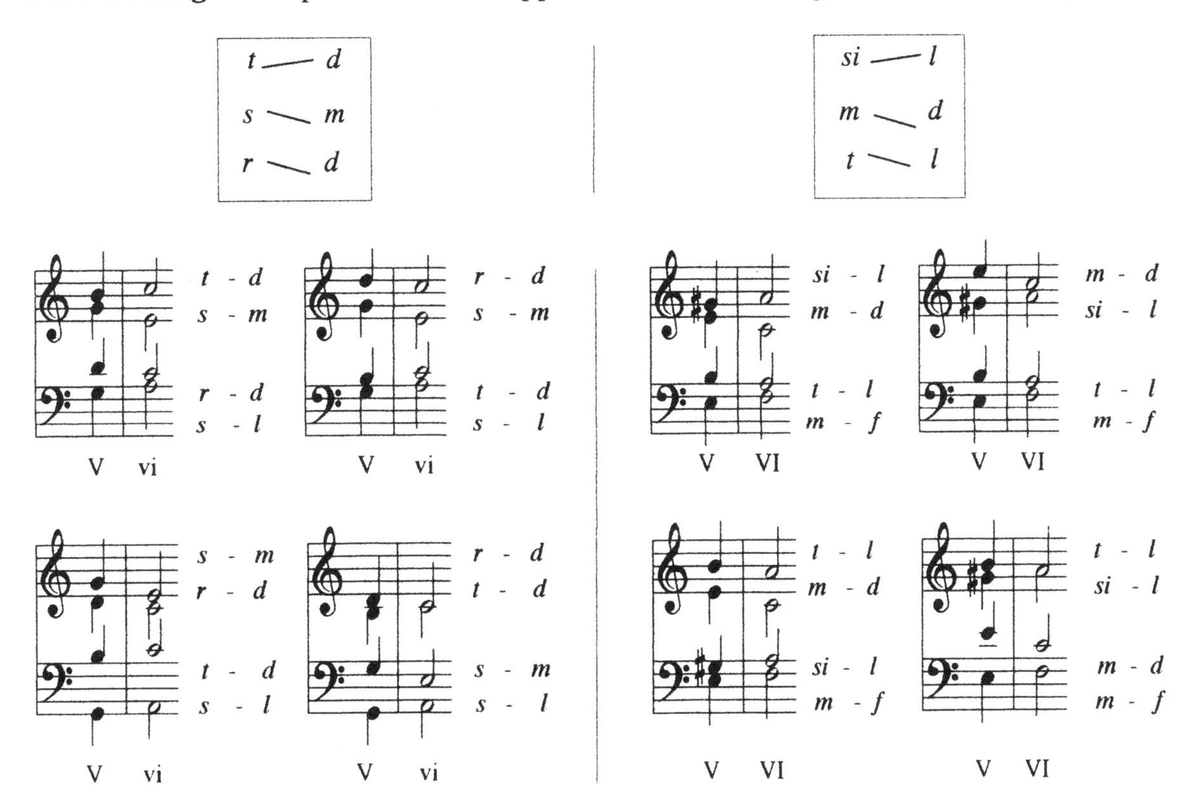

Exercise 66 Finish the chord plans. Add alto and tenor parts to complete these interrupted cadences.

Exercise 67 Complete the chord plans. Add S, A, T in different arrangements.

Exercise 68 Finish the chord plans. Complete these interrupted cadences by adding bass, alto and tenor parts.

Exercise 69 These exercises revise all the cadences learnt so far. For each exercise make a chord plan. Add numerals. Add alto and tenor parts and a cadence name.

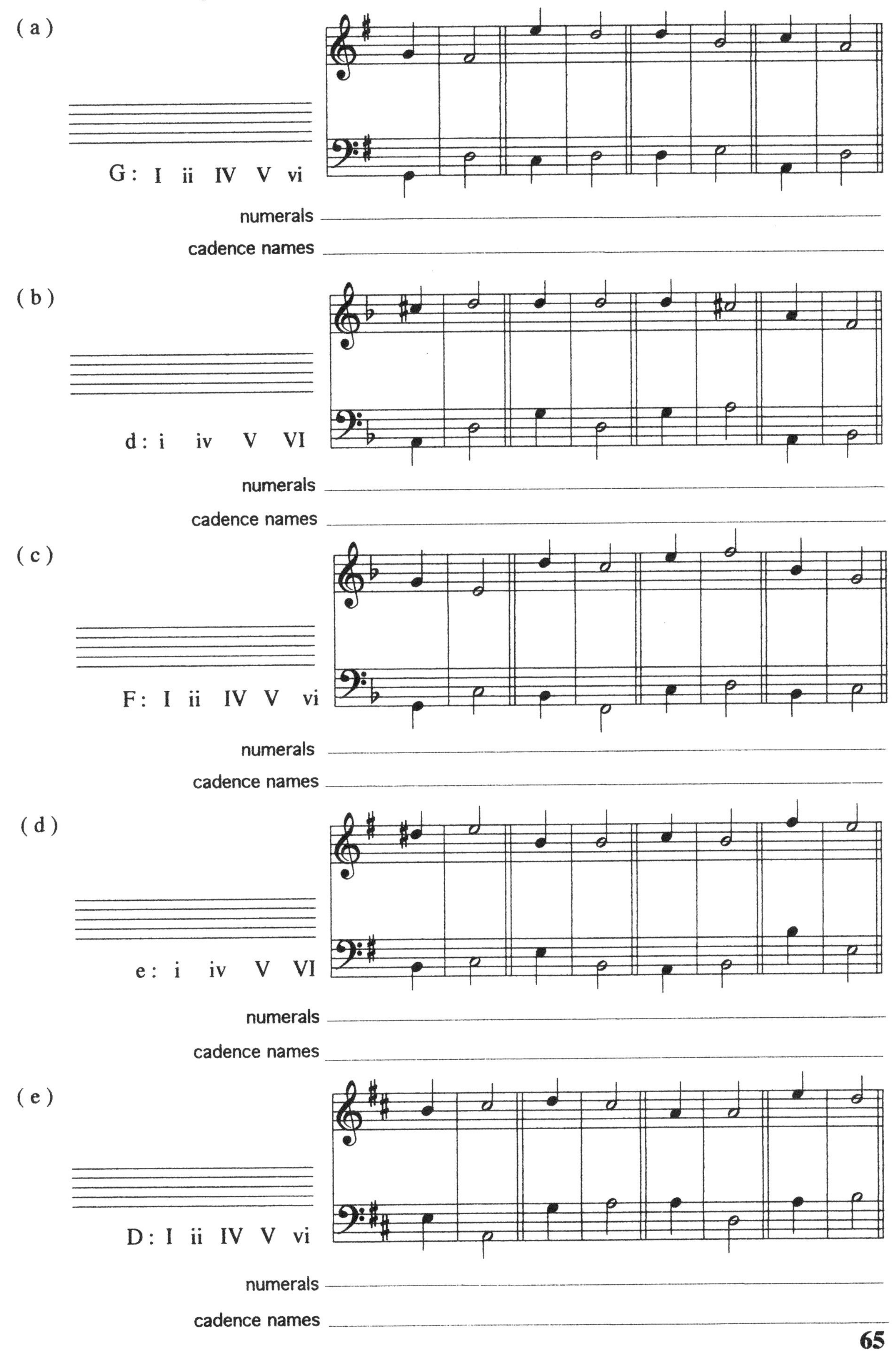

Exercise 70 Each melody has 4 short phrases. Harmonise the bracketed phrase endings to make perfect, imperfect, plagal or interrupted cadences. Each melody is to contain one example of each type of cadence. Make a chord plan. Add solfa names, numerals and cadence names.

(a)

solfa names

D: I ii IV V vi

numerals

cadence names

solfa names

numerals

cadence names

(b)

solfa names

e: i iv V VI

numerals

cadence names

solfa names

numerals

cadence names

Exercise 70 continued

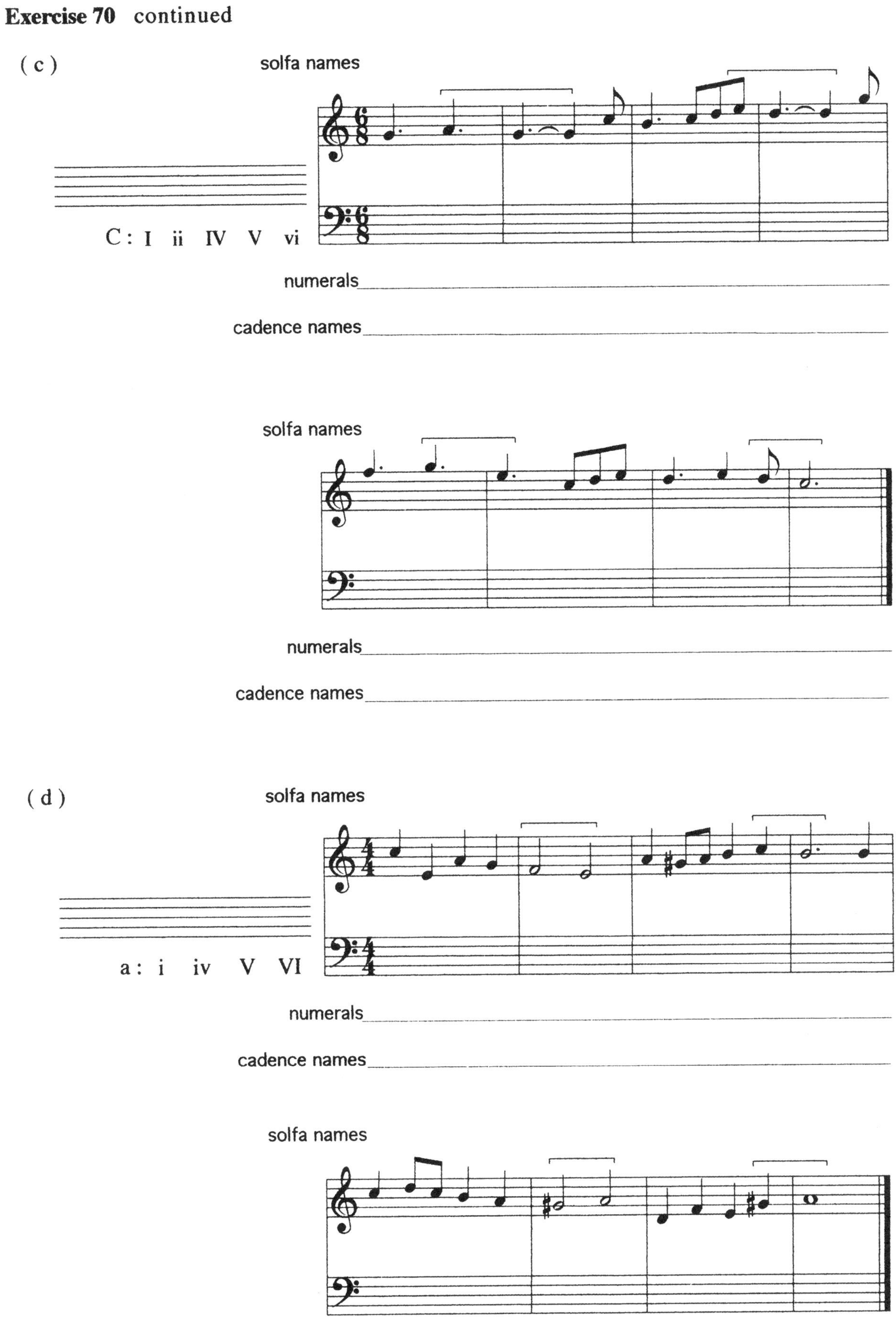

WRITING A MELODY over a GIVEN BASS
Chords : I ii IV V vi in Major Keys : i iv V VI in Minor Keys

- **Chords** More new progressions may now be included in the given bass. Common among these are VI-II and VI-IV. These are often coupled with V - I creating such familiar progressions as VI - II - V - I and VI - IV - V - I. These progressions give a very strong harmonic character and are well illustrated in the final bars of the '*Hornpipe*' from Handel's '*Water Music*'.

  Since the original music uses some chords in inversions and includes various decorative notes not yet studied, a simplified version has also been provided to help you to follow the progressions more easily and with greater clarity. Listen to both versions as you study the analysis given.

Melody Take special care with the direction of the melody over progressions IV - V and V - VI. Otherwise smooth melodic links at chord changes are as important as before.

Listen to this simple piece in A minor and then study the points made about it.

a) The * at the progression V - VI serves as a reminder for careful melodic movement here.

b) The addition of many passing and auxiliary notes has created a shape that is almost entirely stepwise. The leap in bar 3 therefore gives a welcome relief.

c) Compare the overall shape of the treble and bass. There is a good deal of contrary motion. Lines which create a general contrary motion shape have a greater sense of strength and independence than those which 'shadow' one another in the same direction.

Exercise 71 The framework of each tune uses only chord notes. For each, make a chord plan. Add numerals. Rewrite each, adding passing and auxiliary notes where suitable.

Exercise 72 Complete the chord plans and add numerals below the bass roots. Continue each melody from the given opening. When you have finished writing, play each completed piece.

PART 3

D♯ and A♯ MINOR SCALES

■ Revise minor scales and key signatures on page 75 of *Music Workout, Grade 6.*

● This is the scale of F♯ major, followed by its relative minor D♯ in harmonic and melodic forms.

In both forms of the D♯ minor scale notice that, because the 7th note (leading note) is already sharpened, it becomes C double sharp when raised a semitone.

Using a key signature, D♯ minor scale is written like this:

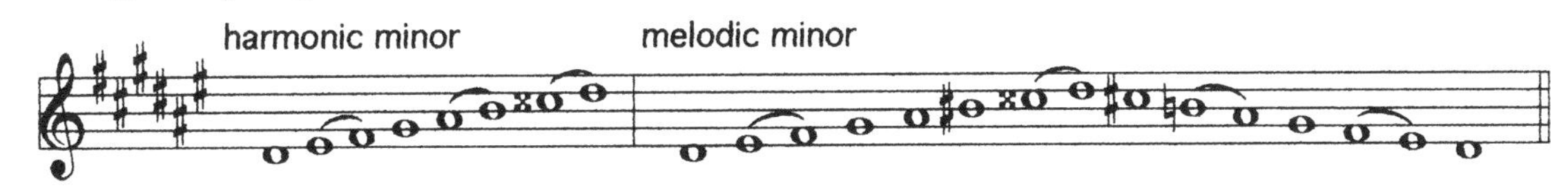

● This is the scale of C♯ major, followed by its relative minor A♯ in harmonic and melodic forms.

Using a key signature, A♯ minor scale is written like this:

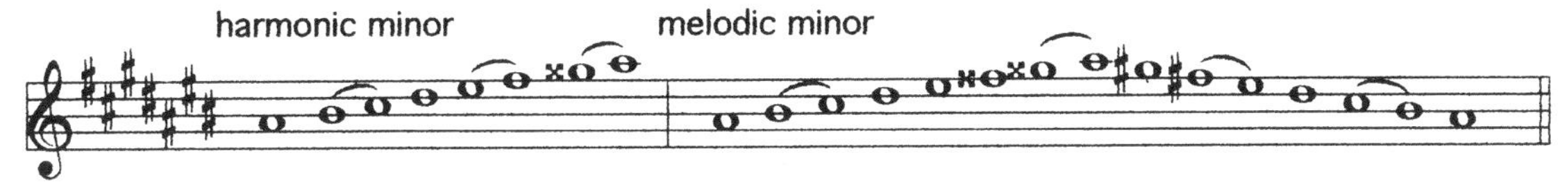

Exercise 73 Using a key signature and the bass clef, write the scale of D♯ minor and A♯ minor in melodic form, ascending and descending.

(a)

(b)

E♭ and A♭ MINOR SCALES

- This is the scale of G♭major followed by its relative minor E♭ in harmonic and melodic minor forms.

Using a key signature, E♭minor scale is written like this :

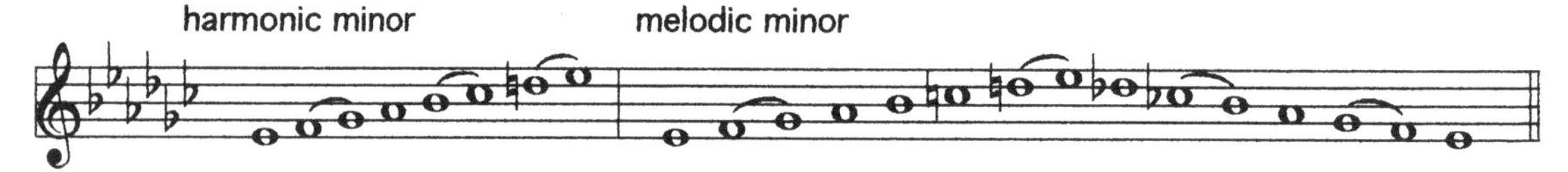

Notice that, when raised, the 6th and 7th notes become <u>naturals</u> .

- This is the scale of C♭ major, followed by its relative minor A♭ in harmonic and melodic forms.

Using a key signature, A♭ minor scale is written like this:

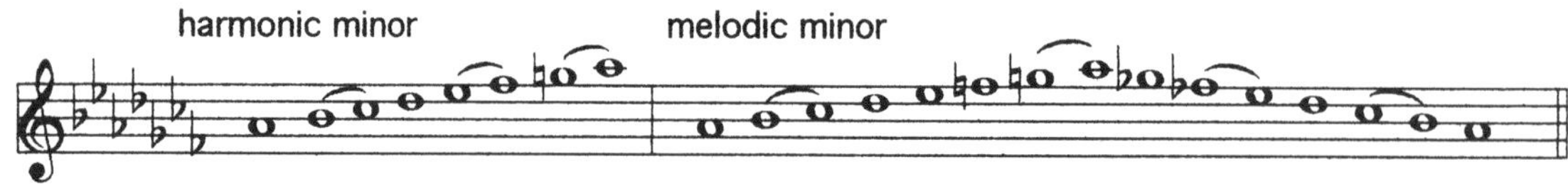

Exercise 74 Write the scales of E♭ minor and A♭ minor ascending and descending in melodic form in the bass clef. Use a key signature.

(a)

(b)

A PAGE of MINOR SCALES

Exercise 75 Add the clef and key signature / accidentals as directed to make these minor scales. Mark the semitones. Draw the tonic triad with accidentals.

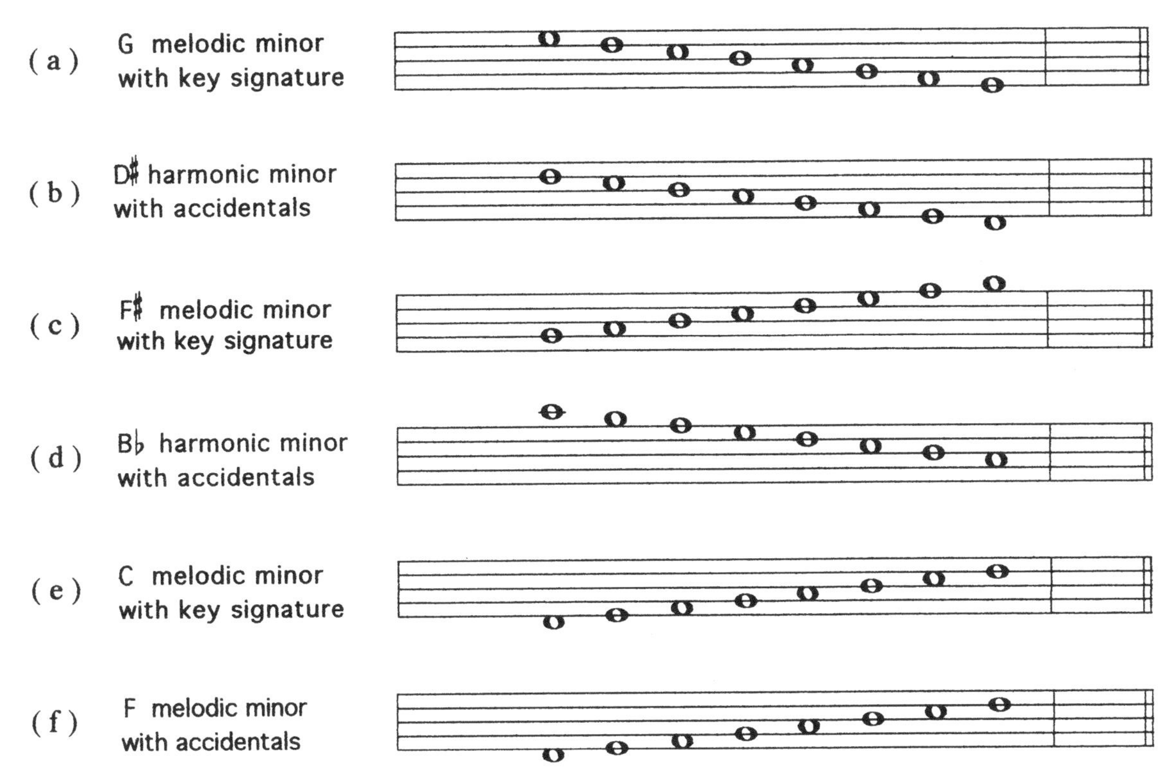

Exercise 76 Write one octave, ascending only, of each of the minor scales of which the key signature is given. State which scale form you are using.

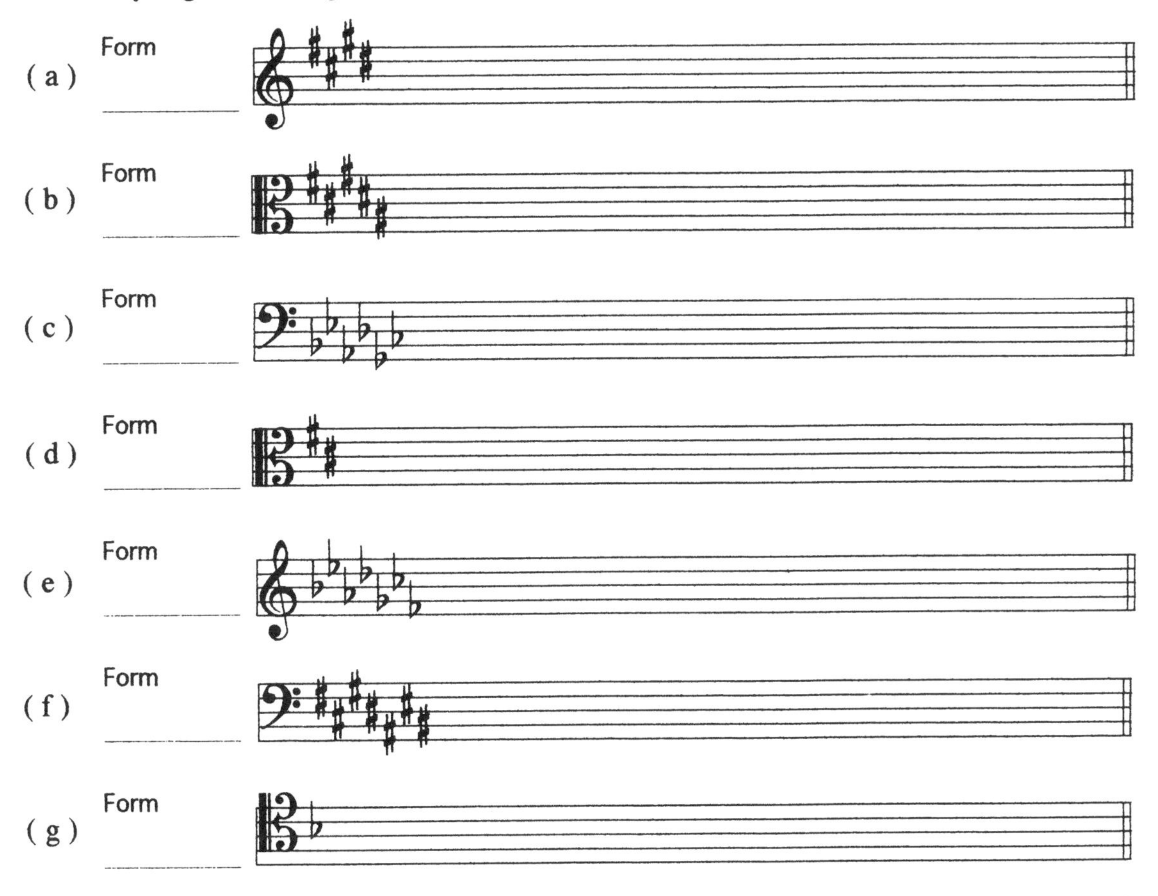

COMPOUND INTERVALS

- An interval greater than an octave is called a **compound interval.**

In the following examples, each interval has been increased in size by one octave.

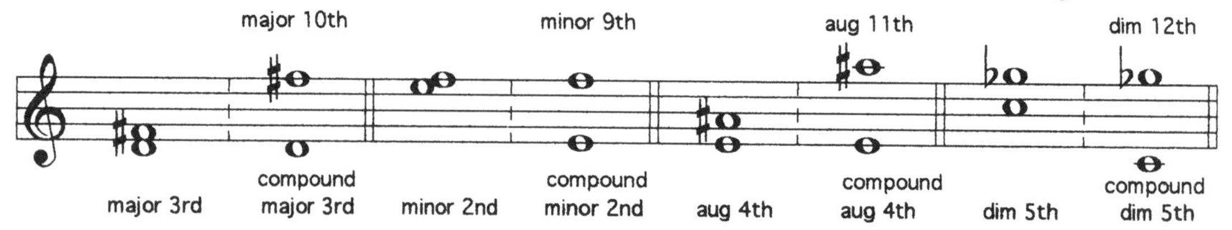

Notice the two sets of names for compound intervals e.g.'compound major 3rd' or 'major 10th'. Of these names, choose the one you prefer, but the lower set may be easier.

To measure a compound interval, reduce its size by an octave. In this example, the reduced interval is a perfect 5th, so the compound interval is a compound perfect 5th .

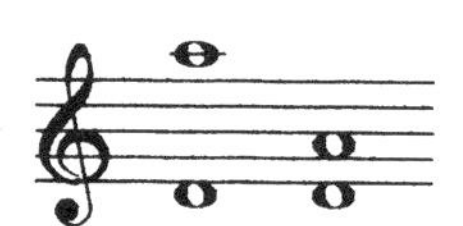

Exercise 77 Name these compound intervals.

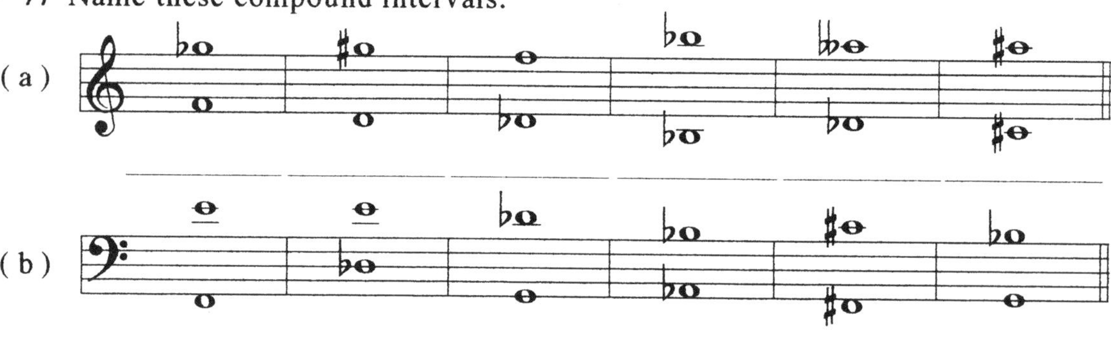

Exercise 78 Compound intervals can also be measured between notes on different staves. Name each of these intervals.

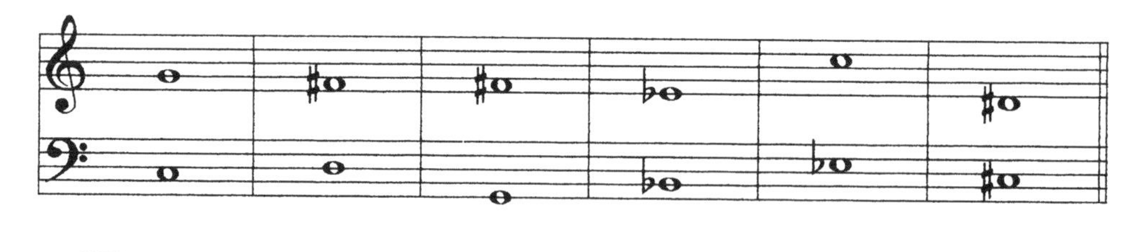

Exercise 79 Above each note draw another to form these compound intervals.

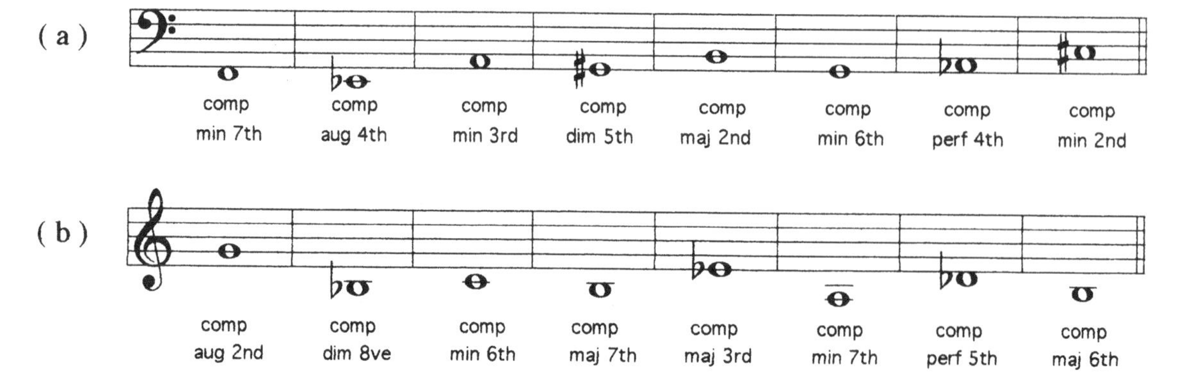

TRANSPOSITION : MAJOR KEYS

■ When transposing music from one key to another, remember these points:

1 The interval of transposition is the interval between the tonic of the original key and the tonic of the new key. (NB: Melodies do not always begin on the tonic.)

2 Do not confuse major/minor intervals of transposition with major/minor keys.

3 Major keys transpose to major keys. Minor keys transpose to minor keys.

● In Grade 6 you learnt how to transpose major and minor melodies up or down by various intervals. These were: major 2nd, major/minor 3rd, perfect 4th/5th. Now the remaining intervals of transposition are added. These are : minor 2nd, major/minor 6th and 7th, all augmented and diminished intervals.

■ Before doing the exercises which follow, revise the pages in '*Music Workout Gr 6*' on measuring intervals: pp 6, 7 and 23. See also page 26 on transposition.

Exercise 80 i) Name the major key for each signature. Then write its tonic. ii) Transpose each note putting in the new signature and naming the new tonic, as in the first two examples.

Take special care when transposing up or down a minor 2nd. Though the distance is a semitone, the new key must have a different letter name to the original key. In the example F♯, not G♭, is a minor 2nd below G.

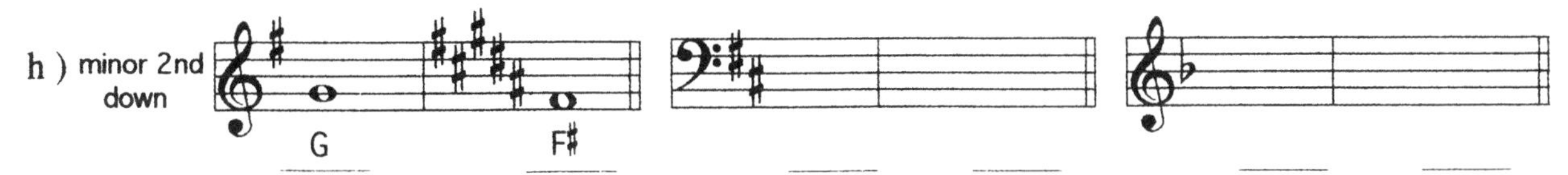

TRANSPOSITION : MINOR KEYS / ACCIDENTALS

● On page75 we studied major key transposition. Now we deal with minor keys.

Exercise 81 i) Name the minor key for each signature and write its tonic. ii) Transpose each note putting in the new signature and naming the new key.

■ Remember that minor keys transpose to minor keys.

● **Accidentals** In any melody an accidental may be a chromatic note (a note which does not belong to the key) or the raised 6th or 7th (*fi* or *si*) of a minor key. We will take an example to illustrate this. Follow these three steps.

Suppose this melody is to be transposed up an augmented 5th.

1 Original key The key signature is that of A ♭ major. But the presence of *fi* and *si* and the final tonic *l* indicate the relative, F minor. The notes marked * are chromatic.

2 New key The interval of transposition is to be an augmented 5th.

i) Count up an augmented 5th from the note F - it is C♯.

ii) Minor keys transpose to minor keys, so the new key is C♯ minor.

iii) Put in the new key signature. Move all notes up a 5th, omitting accidentals.

3 Accidentals Review each accidental in the original melody. Does it raise, lower or restore the note? Accordingly, raise (R), lower (L) or restore (N) in the new key.

TRANSPOSITION EXERCISES : MAJOR / MINOR

Exercise 82 These extracts are to be transposed as directed. For each :

i) Name the key.
ii) Measure accurately the interval of transposition.
iii) Name the new key and put in the correct key signature.
iv) Add accidentals, taking care with their function (raising, lowering or restoring).

TRANSPOSITION with CLEF CHANGE

■Transposition up or down an octave with a clef change has been studied in *Music Workout Gr 6*. See page 33, if revision is necessary.

● Now transposition by other intervals is combined with a clef change. This becomes necessary when a transposition is likely to result in many ledger notes. The use of a clef change can make reading much easier. Study this example.

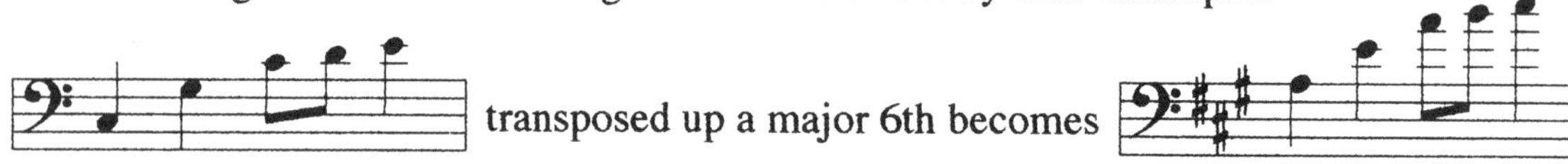

This can be more neatly written as :

Exercise 83 Transpose the given tonic as directed. Write the new tonic in 4 clefs; see (a) below.

Exercise 84 Transpose each melody as directed, writing it on the given stave.

Exercise 84 continued

THE CLASSICAL PERIOD

To give a detailed account of the period is beyond the scope of this book. The aim must be to provide pointers to guide you when beginning your own research. Use the resources available to find out about the composers, music and culture of the time. Try your school or local library for books, tapes and videos. Surf the internet, if you have a suitable computer. Above all, listen to the music of the period.

classical / Classical This term has several meanings when applied to music. With a small 'c ' it denotes work of excellence in any genre; it can also mean music which is not jazz or 'pop'. Classical with a large 'C' refers to works written between 1750 and 1820 or thereabouts, i.e. after the Baroque period and before the heyday of Romantic music in mid-to-late19th C. It is also known as the 'first Viennese Period' as its great composers, Haydn, Mozart, Beethoven and Schubert worked in Vienna about this time. Beethoven died in1827; Schubert helped carry his coffin not knowing he would die within a year.

Style and Texture In contrast with Baroque works, the music of the Classical period, like the literature and architecture of the time, is notable for its beauty of line and form. Balance and control replaced the intricacy of Baroque writing, and melody above a chordal accompaniment became more significant. Phrasing became more clear-cut with defined cadences. In dynamics and keys there was more interest in variety and contrast.

Instrumental music Purely instrumental music became more important than works for voice, though there was much significant composition in both opera and church music. Some new instruments were added e.g. the clarinet and trombone but the major technical innovation was in the pianoforte. The piano with its pedals and dampers was developed to meet the need for contrast of soft/loud, legato/staccato, and cantabile playing, features which interested the Classical composer. The harpsichord was gradually replaced by the more flexible piano. The orchestra, which continued to grow by the addition of woodwind and brass, really became an independent instrument in its own right. For composers the symphony was one of the orchestra's most defined forms of composition.

Vocal music Gluck reformed **opera** by making it a more continuous type of music-drama with less distinction between 'recitative', the conversation or action part, and the 'aria', the solo song part. Mozart used the orchestra to great effect in his operas. He also developed the 'ensemble' when all the major characters sing at once, each voicing their reaction to a situation. In catholic churches, particularly in the Hapsburg lands, the **Mass** was sung by choir, soloists and orchestra - Haydn and Mozart were the main composers. Haydn, Mozart and Beethoven also wrote **solo songs** or **'lieder'**, but Schubert was the first great composer of this genre. In a 'lied' voice and piano become equal partners. In a **song-cycle** a group of poems linked by the same idea, or written by the same poet, is set to music.

Form Another word for form is 'structure'. The **sonata** is an example of form in music. Introduced during the Baroque Period, it was, at first, a piece to be played rather than sung, in contrast to the **cantata**. For the Classical composer, the sonata had a defined form consisting of 3 or more contrasting movements, played by 1 or 2 instruments. Later, sonatas played by larger groups were named by the number of players, e.g. trio, quartet, etc. Such music is known as **chamber music**. A four-movement sonata for orchestra is a **symphony**; a **concerto** is a 3-movement sonata for soloist and orchestra. Because the sonata is so important in the music of the Classical Period and has influenced the later development of music, you should know these ideas and terms.

Sonata form This is the form used in the 1st movements of sonatas, chamber music, symphonies and concertos. It is sometimes known as **first movement form** for this reason. It is also the form of many overtures. It has a 3-part or ternary structure consisting of three sections which follow one another without a break. These are

EXPOSITION	1st subject (tonic)	Bridge (transition)	2nd subject (dominant or relative major)		
DEVELOPMENT	1st and 2nd subjects in assorted keys with some new material				
RECAPITULATION	1st subject (tonic)	Bridge (transition)	2nd subject (tonic)	(Cadenza)	Coda

The **cadenza** is the section of a concerto where the soloist displays his skill; it comes near the end of the 1st or 3rd movement. The **coda** is a tail-piece, providing a suitable ending.

Minuet and Trio The structure of the 3rd movement of a classical symphony has a 'sandwich' form, consisting of a minuet, a contrasting minuet which used originally to be written for 3 instruments (hence the name), and a return to the original minuet.

Rondo A piece with a recurring theme (A), e.g. ABACADA ; it is usually rather jolly. The last movement of a sonata, symphony or concerto often uses rondo form.

SUGGESTIONS FOR RESEARCH

Exercise 85 Find out as much basic information as you can about these composers, for instance when and where they lived and worked. Include the names and dates of some of their most notable works. Present the information in a chart.

C P E Bach J C Bach Gluck Haydn Mozart Beethoven Schubert

Exercise 86 Write a short essay about 'Classicism' in music, architecture and literature. Illustrate your work with quotations and pictures.

Exercise 87 Draw a chart of the basic orchestra you were likely to find in Vienna at the end of 18th century. Using different colours, show new instruments which might have been added later and where they would have been fitted in.

Exercise 88 i. Explain what you mean by the word '*opera* '.
ii. Explain these terms: *recitative*, *aria*, *ensemble*.
iii. What is a '*singspiel*' ?

Exercise 89 List the 5 main parts of the catholic Mass for which Classical composers such as Mozart and Haydn wrote. Give an approximate translation of each Latin name, e.g. *Credo* - 'I believe in God...' etc.

Exercise 90 Give a detailed description of 'sonata form' in relation to any sonata movement by one of the major Classical composers.

Exercise 91 Describe each of these musical forms. Make clear in your answer what they have in common and how they are different.

sonata concerto symphony

INTRODUCING SCORE READING

- You are familiar with the idea of a score. Chords arranged for S.A.T.B. voices are written in a score. Where voices share staves, it is called 'short score'; where each voice has a separate stave, it is 'open score'. Instrumental scores were introduced when you identified chords in excerpts from string quartets. To define the word precisely, a **score** means an orderly arrangement of notes and other signs on one or more staves.

Study the following to refresh your memory. Notice that voices and instruments are arranged from the highest to lowest in sound. For tenor voices '8' under the treble clef shows that the music is to be written an 8ve higher than it sounds.

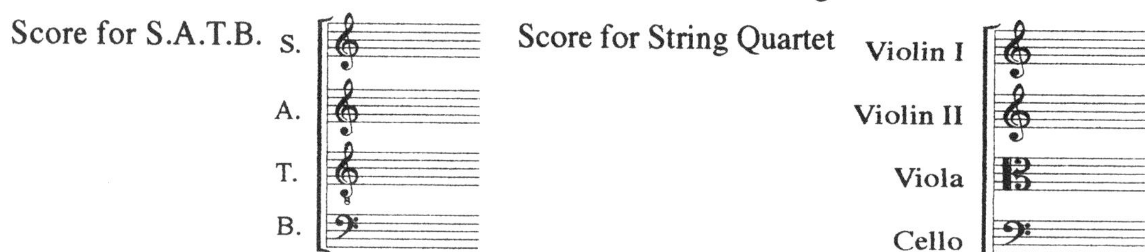

In the next pages we will study scores in more detail, how they are arranged and the conventions used when writing them. But before doing so it is necessary to learn something of how score writing developed. To do this we will consider a little of the history of orchestral composition and performance.

The Baroque Period Orchestral music uses mainly stringed instruments with occasional woodwind (flutes,oboes or bassoons), brass (trumpets or a horn) and percussion (timpani). The harpsichord plays throughout, providing the 'continuo' part which doubles the cello/double bass line and also fills out the harmonies.

The Classical Period Pairs of woodwind instruments become standard (2 flutes, 2 oboes, 2 clarinets, 2 bassoons). This means that the woodwind section can now be used in self-contained 4-part passages. The harpsichord ceases to be necessary, and a pair of horns, capable of playing long sustained notes, keep the texture together. Sometimes a pair of trumpets and timpani (tuned to the tonic and dominant notes) are included.

The 19th Century Romanticism reaches its peak. The orchestra grows in size as new instruments are added to achieve additional effects: in woodwind (piccolo, cor anglais, bass clarinet, double bassoon). Trombones, hitherto used in theatres and churches become standard in the orchestra and a fourth brass instrument, the tuba, is invented and completes the 4-part brass group. Percussion instruments become more varied and numerous. To balance the strengthened sound of other sections, the number of string players is increased.

The 20th Century At the beginning of the century, the size of orchestras can be very large with extra brass and triple or quadruple woodwind. In reaction to the growth in orchestra size, smaller groupings become more common. Present day composers write for varied combinations of instruments and new ways of writing require novel kinds of notation for the special effects composers seek.

SCORE ARRANGEMENT

Order In any orchestral score, from Bach to the present day, the instruments are arranged down the page by family - first woodwind, then brass, percussion and strings. Except for percussion, within each family, instruments are normally arranged downwards in pitch. If a harp, solo instrument, singer or choir is used, this part comes between the percussion and the strings.

Parts Whereas the conductor's score includes all the staves for all the instruments playing, an individual player only sees his/her 'part'. For instance, a cello player's part consists only of the lines of music to be played by the cellos.

Sharing staves Pairs of woodwind or brass instruments share a stave, for example two flutes. Sometimes three such instruments may share a stave.

Sharing desks The music stand used to hold orchestral music is called a 'desk'. As a rule woodwind and brass players have individual desks because they often play individual melodies. String players share desks and music by sitting in pairs.

Clefs The majority of orchestral instruments use the treble clef. The bass clef is used by bassoons, bass trombone and tuba, timpani, cellos and double basses. Violas use the alto clef, while the tenor clef is used for some higher notes of bassoons and cellos as well as for the tenor trombone. No clefs are used for non-pitched percussion instruments which use a single-line stave.

Special effects and markings Watch out for the following :

1 WOODWIND and BRASS

'a 2' or **zu 2'** : Both instruments sharing the stave play the tune which follows.

'1' : The 1st player of a pair plays the melody alone. **'1'** is only needed after an **'a 2'** passage. Normally a single line of melody is played by the 1st player without any special marking.

2 BRASS

'Con sordino'/ 'senza sordino': With mute / without mute. A cone is put into or taken from the bell of the instrument.The mute gives a distant, muffled sound.

3 STRINGS

'pizzicato': The string is plucked, not played with the bow.

'arco' : Play with the bow, after a pizzicato passage.

'double stopping' : 'Stopping' means pressing a string down on the fingerboard. When 2 strings are pressed down, 2 sounds are produced simultaneously.

'Con sordino'/ 'senza sordino': With mute / without mute. A mute for strings is a small clamp placed on the bridge of the instrument.

'div' = divisi : Where 2 or more notes are to be played simultaneously and doublestopping is not feasible, the players divide themselves into groups, each group playing one note.

'unis' : All play the same note. Used after a 'div' passage.

𝅗𝅥 = **'tremolo'** : The rapid reiteration of a note by back and forth bow strokes. The short double beam across the minim stem means that semiquavers to the value of a minim are to be played, e.g. ♬♬ ♬♬
Tremolo can also be in quavers or in demisemiquavers.

FOREIGN NAMES for INSTRUMENTS and KEYS

- Scores usually name the orchestral instruments in Italian, just as other markings are commonly given in this language. German and French may also be used, so it is necessary to know the names of instruments in several languages. Study the list below and make a note of the more unusual foreign names which it can be difficult to guess at. To help you, the trickier ones are printed in heavy type.

	ENGLISH	ITALIAN	GERMAN	FRENCH
WOODWIND	Piccolo	**Flauto piccolo**	**Kleine Flöte**	**Petite flûte**
	Flute	Flauto	Flöte	Flûte
	Oboe	Oboe	Hoboe	**Hautbois**
	Cor anglais	**Corno inglese**	**Englisches Horn**	Cor anglais
	Clarinet	Clarinetto	Klarinette	Clarinette
	Bass clarinet	Clarinetto basso	Bassklarinette	Clarinette basse
	Bassoon	**Fagotto**	**Fagott**	Basson
	Double bassoon	**Contrafagotto**	**Contrafagott**	**Contrebasson**
BRASS	Horn	**Corno**	Horn	**Cor**
	Trumpet	**Tromba**	Trompete	Trompette
	Trombone	Trombone	**Posaune**	Trombone
	Tuba	Tuba	Tuba	Tuba
PERCUSSION	Kettledrums	Timpani	**Pauken**	**Timbales**
	Bass drum	**Gran cassa**	**Grosse Trommel**	**Grosse caisse**
	Snare(side) drum	**Tamburo militare**	**Kleine Trommel**	**Tambour militaire**
	Cymbals	**Piatti**	**Becken**	Cymbales
	Triangle	Triangolo	Triangel	Triangle
	Tambourine	Tamburino	**Schellentrommel**	**Tambour de Basque**
	Tubular bells	**Campanelle**	**Glocken**	**Cloches**
	Glockenspiel	**Campanetta**	Glockenspiel	**Carillon**
	Xylophone	**Zilafone**	Xylophon	Xylophone
	Celesta	Celesta	Celesta	Celeste
	Harp	Arpa	Harfe	Harpe
STRINGS	Violin I	Violino I	Violine I	Violon I
	Violin II	Violino II	Violine II	Violon II
	Viola	Viola	**Bratsche**	**Alto**
	Cello	Violoncello	Violoncell	Violoncelle
	Double bass	**Contrabasso**	**Kontrabass**	**Contrebasse**

- **Foreign names for keys** Key names are different in other languages. You will meet them in titles and names of transposing instruments, so you should learn them.

ENGLISH	ITALIAN	GERMAN	FRENCH
Major	Maggiore	**Dur**	Majeur
Minor	Minore	**Moll**	Mineur
A	**La**	A	**La**
B	**Si**	**H**	**Si**
C	**Do**	C	**Do**
D	**Re**	D	**Ré**
E	**Mi**	E	**Mi**
F	**Fa**	F	**Fa**
G	**Sol**	G	**Sol**
Sharp	**Diesis**	'**is**' is added to the letter: e.g. **C♯** = **Cis**	**Dièse**
Flat	**Bemolle**	'**es**' or '**s**' is added to the letter: e.g. **D♭** = **Des** (exception: **B♭** = **B**)	**Bémol**

- **Transposing instruments** This is a summary of the principal transposing instruments showing their sounds in relation to a written C. (See *Music Workout Grade 6* pp 50 - 51)

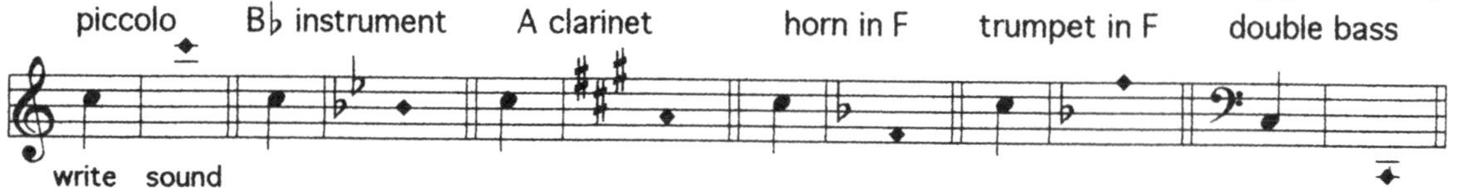

SCORE READING EXERCISES

Exercise 92 Study this extract from Schubert's Symphony No 4. Then answer the questions.

1 a The orchestral family at the foot of the score is? ______________________

b Give the English names of the instruments in this section.

____

____

____

____

____

c The letter name of the first note sounded by clarinets is ______

d The letter name of the first note played by 2nd oboes is ______

2 a In bars 1 - 4 cellos and ______________________ are playing in unison.

b In bars 1 - 4 the instruments sounding an octave lower than the cellos are the ______________________

3 a Explain why 'a 2' appears above the bassoon stave. ______________________

____

b Explain '1' above the flute stave. ______________________

Exercise 93 Study this extract from a Mozart Piano Concerto. Then answer the questions.

1 i Mozart omits one orchestral family from this concerto. Which is it? ______________

ii In this excerpt, another family is represented by only one instrument. Name the family and the instrument. Family ________________ Instrument ________________

iii In the first half of the extract, one important group of instruments is not playing. Which group is it? ________________

2 *Klavier* is the German word for 'keyboard'. Here it means the piano. Having studied the piano part, fill in the blanks in these sentences.

i Bar ____ contains only notes of the tonic chord.

ii The 4 chords marked * in bar 7 are __________ __________ __________ __________

iii Bar 8 contains part of a ________________ scale.

3 i Explain 'Tutti' over the flute stave. ________________________________

ii Which instruments repeat bars 1 and 2 of the piano melody? ________________

Exercise 94 This is an extract from Beethoven's Symphony No 9 ('Choral'). Study the music, then answer the questions.

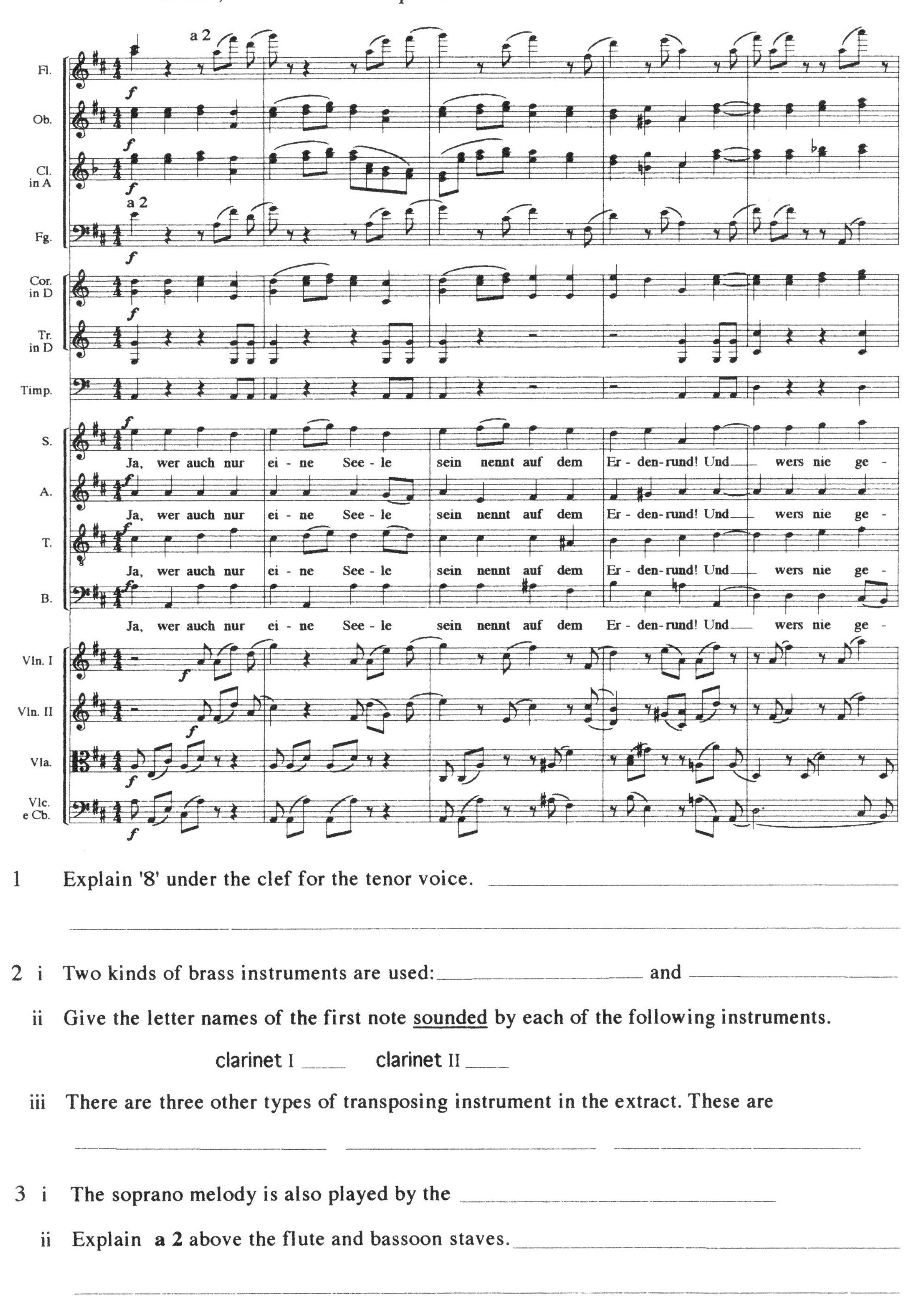

1 Explain '8' under the clef for the tenor voice. ______________________

____

2 i Two kinds of brass instruments are used: ______________ and ______________

ii Give the letter names of the first note <u>sounded</u> by each of the following instruments.

clarinet I ____ clarinet II ____

iii There are three other types of transposing instrument in the extract. These are

______________ ______________ ______________

3 i The soprano melody is also played by the ______________________

ii Explain **a 2** above the flute and bassoon staves. ______________________

____

Exercise 95 Study this excerpt from Tchaikovsky's 'Nutcracker Suite'. It is the opening of the 'Trepak', a Russian dance. Then answer the questions.

Tempo di trepak, molto vivace

Flauti I
Flauti II. III
Oboi I II
Corno Inglese
Clarinrtto I in A
Clarinetto II in A
Clar. Basso in B
Fagotti I II
Corni I. II in F
Corni III. IV in F
Trombe in A
Tromboni Tenori
Tr. Basso e Tuba
Timpani G. D
Tamburino
Violino I
Violino II
Viole
Celli
C. Bassi

1 Give the English names for these instruments listed on the score.

Corno inglese ____________

Corni ____________

Fagotti ____________

Trombe ____________

Contrabassi ____________

Tr. Basso ____________

2 i Give the letter names of the first note sounded by:

Clarinet I	☐	Clarinet II	☐
Horn I	☐	Horn II	☐
Horn III	☐	Horn IV	☐

2 ii Name 2 other transposing instruments used in this excerpt.

____

____

3 i How many different woodwind instruments are needed to play this music? ________

ii How many types of brass instruments are listed? ________

iii How many types of percussion instruments are used? ________

4 The piece which precedes this one in the 'Nutcracker Suite' ends with most of the strings playing 'pizz'. Now the players have to play 'arco'. Explain these two terms.

pizz. ____________ arco ____________

5 i Why does the tambourine use a single line stave? ____________

ii The alto clef is used by ____________ iii The tenor clef is used by ____________

HARMONIC ANALYSIS

Your harmonic knowledge will now be broadened through analysing music which uses a wider range of chords than you have been writing up to this. You will meet chords in inversions as well as in root position and learn to recognise them by sight and sound in preparation for using them in your own written work in the next grade. Chord analysis is linked to aural/visual observation pieces to underline the importance of listening to chords in a real musical context; see pages 90 - 93.

The dominant 7th You already know the dominant chord (V). This chord may be extended by adding a 7th above its root making a richer sound. When the 7th is added to the chord, a small '7' is attached to the roman numeral as shown in the example.

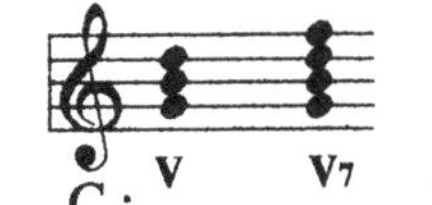

The sound of V_7 is distinctive and gives the music a sense of forward movement. You hear it used frequently in music of all styles.

Chords in 1st inversion A triad or chord is in1st inversion when its 3rd is the lowest sound. 1st inversion chords give more variety in the harmony and create a more gentle flowing effect than do root position chords alone. A small 'b' is attached to the roman numeral to indicate that a chord is in 1st inversion.

The texture of vocal music varies from that of instrumental music. In the latter it is common to find chords arranged for any number of parts by duplicating notes at different pitches. However, the position of a chord is always determined by its lowest note.

The range of chords to be recognised in 1st inversion in major and minor keys is:

Ib	* IIb	IVb	Vb

* In minor keys, chord ii is a diminished chord and is more commonly used in 1st inversion.

Chords in 2nd inversion A triad or chord is in 2nd inversion when its 5th is the lowest sound. A small 'c' attached to the numeral shows that a chord is in 2nd inversion.

A common use of the 2nd inversion chord is to decorate a cadence, e.g. Ic V. This progression is sometimes called a ' **cadential 6/4 on the dominant** ' as Ic consists of the intervals of a 6th and a 4th above the dominant bass note.

Listen to the cadence and notice how: (i) Ic gives the effect of 'leaning' onto V. (ii) Ic and V share the same bass note.

Local Centre Exams Syllabus note	In Aural Tests for Grade 7 practical examinations, questions 1 - 3 may be asked. In Grade 7 written Theory examinations, question 4* (harmonic analysis) replaces question 3.

Aural/Visual Observation Questions These are to be done orally. They combine aural/visual observation with harmonic analysis. All questions should be worked through.

Exercise 96 Follow the music, which should be played twice. Then answer the questions.

1 i Name the tonic key. ii Name the relative of the tonic. iii Name the dominant key.

2 i In bars 9 to12 the style of the music changes. Describe what happens in these bars.

ii The texture of the music is typical of the Baroque period to which Corelli belongs. Is the overall texture: contrapuntal? chordal? melody with accompaniment?

3 i Point out an imperfect cadence in the piece. If necessary, have it played again.

ii To which key has the music modulated by bar 8?

iii At which point do you think the music returns to the tonic key?

* ——————————————————————————————— *

4 i Identify the chords boxed with dotted lines in bars 2,14 and 15.

ii The circled notes are either passing notes or auxiliary notes. Describe each.

Exercise 97 Have this minuet played twice while you follow the music. Then answer the questions below.

1 i Name the tonic key. ii Name the relative of the tonic. iii Name the dominant key.

2 i Describe how the passage from bar 9 to bar 12 differs from the rest of the piece.

ii Does the opening phrase return?

iii The texture of most of the music is very simple. Would you describe it as :

Melody with accompaniment ? Chordal ? Contrapuntal ?

3 i Point out an imperfect cadence in the piece. If necessary, have it played again.

ii Where does a modulation occur? To which key does the music modulate?

iii In which bar do you feel the music has returned to the tonic key?

——

4 i Identify the four chords marked with asterisks in bars 9 - 12.

ii In which bar can you find Ic -V_7 i.e.the cadential 6/4 on the dominant, followed by the dominant 7th ?

iii The circled notes are either passing notes or auxiliary notes. Describe each.

Exercise 98 Having had the piece played twice while following the music, answer the questions.

1 i Name the tonic key. ii Name the relative of the tonic. iii Name the dominant key.

2 i Compare the melody in bars 1 - 2 with that in bars 3 - 4. What do you notice?

ii In bars 8 - 9 the upper hand (part) "imitates" the lower hand but a bar later. Find two more bars where this happens.

iii Apart from bars 8 - 11, describe the texture of the music. Is it melody with chordal accompaniment? Is it two melodies together?

3 i Point to a perfect cadence in the piece. If necessary, ask for it to be played again.

ii The music modulates to the dominant key. In which bars does this happen?

* ———————————————————————————————— *

4 i Identify chords marked * in bars 1, 2, 3, 13. Use **b** or **c** to indicate inversions.

ii Notes are circled in bars 2, 5, 7, 12. Identify each as a passing or an auxiliary note.

iii Find these chords in the tonic key: tonic, 2nd inv. (the cadential 6/4 on the dominant); dominant 7th chord in root position.

Exercise 99 Have the piece played twice while you follow the music. Then answer the questions. The music has been adapted from a 'Study' by Burgmüller.

1 i Name the tonic key. ii Name the relative of the tonic. iii Name the dominant key.

2 i How would you describe the texture of bars 1 - 8? Choose one of the following:
Contrapuntal ? Melody with accompaniment ?

ii In what way do bars 9 - 16 differ from bars 1 - 8?

iii Are bars 1 - 8 exactly repeated later in the piece?

3 i To which key does the music modulate in bars 5 - 8?

ii Where does the music return to the tonic key?

iii Where can you sense an imperfect cadence?

* ———————————————————————————————— *

4 i Identify the boxed chords.

ii Are all the circled notes: passing notes ? auxiliary notes?

iii In the passage that has modulated find: tonic chord, 2nd inversion ; dominant 7th, root position.

GRADE 7
Syllabus

Keys / Interval Transposition Scales and key signatures of all keys major and minor. All simple and compound intervals. Transposition of a melody by any interval in any of the four clefs.

Melodic Composition Using a given opening to compose a twelve bar melody which should include a modulation to the dominant key or the relative major or minor key; marks of tempo, phrasing and expression to be included.
Or (at the candidate's choice) the setting of words for solo voice.

Harmony Using the following resources :

Major keys C, G, D and F - chords I ii IV V vi
Minor keys A, E and D - chords i iv V VI

in root position with unaccented passing and auxiliary notes.

a) To select suitable chords to harmonise cadential points in a given melody (indicate by roman numerals) and also write the appropriate root notes in the bass.
b) To add inner parts in perfect, imperfect, plagal and interrupted cadences for SATB in which the soprano and bass are given.
c) To write a melody above a given progression of chords. The bass line will be complete and the opening of the melody given.

Harmonic Analysis In a given extract for piano or voices in any major or minor key to identify these chords: tonic, supertonic, subdominant, dominant and submediant, in root position and first inversion; the cadential 6/4 on the dominant; the dominant 7th chord in root position; unaccented passing and auxiliary notes.

History/ Instruments A general knowledge of the Classical period to include style, forms, main composers and their standard works.
General questions on an orchestral extract to include abbreviated and foreign names of instruments.

First published in 2001 by
The Royal Irish Academy of Music
Westland Row, Dublin 2.

©2001 by The Royal Irish Academy of Music

ISBN 1 - 902140 - 08 - 7

All rights reserved. This book or parts thereof may not be reproduced in any form or by any means, electronic or mechanical, including photocopying, recording or any information storage and retrieval system now known or to be invented, without prior permission from the publisher.

Music processing Jean Archibald and Bernadette Marmion
Typesetting and graphics Creighton Music, Dublin 14.
Cover design Origin Design Associates.
Printed by Brunswick Press, Dublin 12.